The Wedding Day

The Wedding Day

in

Literature and Art

*A Collection of the Best Descriptions of Weddings
from the Works of the World's Leading
Novelists and Poets, richly illustrated
with Reproductions of Famous
Paintings of Incidents of
the Nuptial Day*

COMPILED BY

C. F. CARTER, *1863 - 1939*

New York

Dodd, Mead and Company

Detroit: Reissued by Singing Tree Press, Book Tower, 1969

First Published in 1900

Library of Congress Catalog Card Number 74-86598

Preface

BY general consent the wedding day is considered to be the happiest episode in life. An event so rich in human interest, a day so universally filled with feasting and merrymaking, ought to furnish a subject that would call forth the best efforts of the poet, the painter, and the novelist. Singularly enough, the wedding is a topic of which artists and writers seem to be rather wary. As the result of an exhaustive search through all available data, the assertion is ventured that of the many thousands of paintings in existence in Europe and America not more than one hundred and eighty have as their theme incidents of the wedding day. Poets are even more reluctant to treat of the nuptial day than their brethren of the palette and brush, and novelists are scarcely less so.

Fortunately, those who have ventured to depict the events of the wedding day are among the world's foremost authors and artists, so that the inherent interest of the subject, whether portrayed on canvas or the printed page, is usually developed by the hand of a master.

To gather the choicest of these wedding-day masterpieces of painter, poet, and novelist in attractive form is the object of this volume. All appearance of being statistically instructive or painfully comprehensive has been carefully avoided; but in order that those who cannot or will not marry may at least contemplate the conjugal felicity of others from as many points of view as possible a great variety of weddings is respectfully presented. There is the wedding dramatic, the wedding romantic, the sentimental wedding, and the humorous wedding in England, Ireland, Scotland, Norway, France, Italy, India, China, Japan, Australia, and these United States delineated by writers and painters of both sexes in America and Europe.

If this volume serves to call the attention of the novelists of the future to that most fascinating topic, the wedding, so that the reader who hereafter conscientiously plods through some hundreds of pages of lovers' vicissitudes may at last have the satisfaction of seeing the leading characters safely married off, instead of having the cover unceremoniously shut in his face as soon as an "understanding" is reached, as is usually the case, thus leaving him a prey to uncomfortable apprehensions that the heroine may, after all, exercise woman's inalienable right to change her mind, then the labor of compiling it will not have been in vain.

C. F. CARTER.

NEW YORK, July 5, 1899.

Table of Contents

Table of Contents

Table of Contents

Illustrations

xi

Illustrations

The Wedding Day
In Literature and Art

From "THE BELLS"

By EDGAR ALLAN POE

HEAR the mellow wedding bells, —
Golden bells!
What a world of happiness their harmony foretells!
Through the balmy air of night
How they ring out their delight!
From the molten golden notes,
What a liquid ditty floats
To the turtle-dove that listens, while she gloats
On the moon!
Oh, from out the sounding cells,
What a gush of euphony voluminously wells!
How it swells!
How it dwells
On the Future! How it tells
Of the rapture that impels
To the swinging and the ringing
Of the bells, bells, bells,
Of the bells, bells, bells, bells,
Bells, bells, bells, —
To the rhyming and the chiming of the bells!

Wedding Day in Literature and Art

From "DAVID COPPERFIELD"

By CHARLES DICKENS

YES! I am going to be married to Dora! Miss Lavinia and Miss Clarissa have given their consent; and if ever canary birds were in a flutter, they are. Miss Lavinia, self-charged with the superintendence of my darling's wardrobe, is constantly cutting out brown-paper cuirasses, and differing in opinion from a highly respectable young man, with a long bundle, and a yard measure under his arm. A dressmaker, always stabbed in the breast with a needle and thread, boards and lodges in the house; and seems to me — eating, drinking, or sleeping — never to take her thimble off. They make a lay-figure of my dear. They are always sending for her to come and try something on. We can't be happy together for five minutes in the evening, but some intrusive female knocks at the door, and says, "Oh, if you please, Miss Dora, would you step upstairs?"

Miss Clarissa and my aunt roam all over London, to find out articles of furniture for Dora and me to look at. It would be better for them to buy the goods at once, without this ceremony of inspection; for, when we go to see a kitchen fender and meat screen, Dora sees a Chinese house for Jip, with little bells on the top, and prefers that. And it takes a long time to accustom Jip to his new residence, after we have bought it; whenever he goes in or out, he makes all the little bells ring, and is horribly frightened.

Peggotty comes up to make herself useful, and falls to work immediately. Her department appears to be to clean everything over and over again. She rubs everything that can be rubbed, until it shines, like her own honest forehead, with perpetual friction. And now it is that I begin to see her solitary brother passing through the dark streets at

THE HONEYMOON.

Leighton.

night, and looking, as he goes, among the wandering faces. I never speak to him at such an hour. I know too well, as his grave figure passes onward, what he seeks and what he dreads.

Why does Traddles look so important when he calls upon me this afternoon in the Commons — where I still occasionally attend, for form's sake, when I have time? The realisation of my boyish day-dreams is at hand. I am going to take out the license.

It is a little document to do so much; and Traddles contemplates it, as it lies upon my desk, half in admiration, half in awe. There are the names, in the sweet old visionary connection, David Copperfield and Dora Spenlow; and there, in the corner, is that Parental Institution, the Stamp Office, which is so benignantly interested in the various transactions of human life, looking down upon our Union; and there is the Archbishop of Canterbury invoking a blessing on us in print, and doing it as cheap as could possibly be expected.

Nevertheless, I am in a dream, a flustered, happy, hurried dream. I can't believe that it is going to be; and yet I can't believe but that everyone I pass in the street must have some kind of perception that I am to be married the day after to-morrow. The Surrogate knows me, when I go down to be sworn; and disposes of me easily, as if there were a Masonic understanding between us. Traddles is not at all wanted, but is in attendance as my general backer.

" I hope the next time you come here, my dear fellow," I say to Traddles, " it will be on the same errand for yourself. And I hope it will be soon."

" Thank you for your good wishes, my dear Copperfield," he replies. " I hope so, too. It's a satisfaction to know that she 'll wait for me any length of time, and that she really is the dearest girl — "

" When are you to meet her at the coach? " I ask.

" At seven," says Traddles, looking at his plain old silver watch, — the very watch he once took a wheel out of, at school, to make a water-mill. "That is about Miss Wickfield's time, is it not?"

"A little earlier. Her time is half-past eight."

"I assure you, my dear boy," says Traddles, "I am almost as pleased as if I were going to be married myself, to think that this event is coming to such a happy termination. And really the great friendship and consideration of personally associating Sophy with the joyful occasion, and inviting her to be a bridesmaid in conjunction with Miss Wickfield, demands my warmest thanks. I am extremely sensible of it."

I hear him, and shake hands with him; and we talk, and walk, and dine, and so on; but I don't believe it. Nothing is real.

Sophy arrives at the house of Dora's aunts, in due course. She has the most agreeable of faces, — not absolutely beautiful, but extraordinarily pleasant, — and is one of the most genial, unaffected, frank, engaging creatures I have ever seen. Traddles presents her to us with great pride; and rubs his hands for ten minutes by the clock, with every individual hair upon his head standing on tiptoe, when I congratulate him in a corner on his choice.

I have brought Agnes from the Canterbury coach, and her cheerful and beautiful face is among us for the second time. Agnes has a great liking for Traddles, and it is capital to see them meet, and to observe the glory of Traddles, as he commends the dearest girl in the world to her acquaintance.

Still I don't believe it. We have a delightful evening, and are supremely happy; but I don't believe it yet. I can't collect myself. I can't check off my happiness, as it takes place. I feel in a misty and unsettled kind of state; as if I had got up very early in the morning a week or two ago, and had never been to bed since. I can't make out when yesterday was. I seem to have been carrying the license about in my pocket, many months.

Next day, too, when we all go in a flock to see the house — our house — Dora's and mine — I am quite unable to regard myself as its master. I seem to be there by permission of somebody else. I half expect the real master to come home presently, and say he is glad to see me. Such a beautiful little house as it is, with everything so bright and new; with the flowers on the carpets looking as if freshly gathered, and the green leaves on the paper as if they had just come out; with the spotless muslin curtains, and the blushing rose-coloured furniture, and Dora's garden hat with the blue ribbon — do I remember, now, how I loved her in such another hat when I first knew her? — already hanging on its little peg; the guitar-case quite at home on its heels in a corner; and everybody tumbling over Jip's Pagoda, which is much too big for the establishment.

Another happy evening, quite as unreal as all the rest of it, and I steal into the usual room before going away. Dora is not there. I suppose they have not done trying on yet. Miss Lavinia peeps in, and tells me mysteriously that she will not be long. She is rather long, notwithstanding; but by and by I hear a rustling at the door, and someone taps.

I say, " Come in ! " but someone taps again.

I go to the door, wondering who it is; there I meet a pair of bright eyes and a blushing face; they are Dora's eyes and face, and Miss Lavinia has dressed her in to-morrow's dress, bonnet and all, for me to see. I take my little wife to my heart; and Miss Lavinia gives a little scream because I tumble the bonnet, and Dora laughs and cries at once, because I am so pleased; and I believe it less than ever.

" Do you think it pretty, Doady ? " says Dora.

Pretty ! I should rather think I did.

" And are you sure you like me very much ? " says Dora.

The topic is fraught with such danger to the bonnet that Miss Lavinia gives another little scream and begs me to understand that Dora is only to be looked at, and on no account to be touched. So Dora stands in a delightful state of confusion for a minute or two, to be admired, and then takes off her bonnet — looking so natural without it! — and runs away with it in her hand; and comes dancing down again in her own familiar dress, and asks Jip if I have got a beautiful little wife, and whether he'll forgive her for being married, and kneels down to make him stand upon the cookery-book, for the last time in her single life.

I go home, more incredulous than ever, to a lodging that I have hard by; and get up very early in the morning, to ride to the Highgate road and fetch my aunt.

I have never seen my aunt in such state. She is dressed in lavender-coloured silk, and has a white bonnet on, and is amazing. Janet has dressed her, and is there to look at me. Peggotty is ready to go to church, intending to behold the ceremony from the gallery. Mr. Dick, who is to give my darling to me at the altar, has had his hair curled. Traddles, whom I have taken up by appointment at the turnpike, presents a dazzling combination of cream colour and light blue; and both he and Mr. Dick have a general effect about them of being all gloves.

No doubt I see this, because I know it is so; but I am astray, and seem to see nothing. Nor do I believe anything whatever. Still, as we drive along in an open carriage, this fairy marriage is real enough to fill me with a sort of wondering pity for the unfortunate people who have no part in it, but are sweeping out the shops and going to their daily occupations.

My aunt sits with my hand in hers all the way. When we stop a little way short of the church to put down Peggotty, whom we have brought on the box, she gives it a squeeze, and me a kiss.

" God bless you, Trot! My own boy never could be dearer. I think of poor dear Baby this morning."

" So do I. And of all I owe to you, dear aunt."

" Tut, child ! " says my aunt; and gives her hand in overflowing cordiality to Traddles, who then gives his to Mr. Dick, who then gives his to me, who then give mine to Traddles, and then we come to the church-door.

The church is calm enough, I am sure; but it might be a steam-power loom in full action, for any sedative effect it has on me. I am too far gone for that.

The rest is all a more or less incoherent dream.

A dream of them coming in with Dora; of the pew-opener arranging us, like a drill sergeant, before the altar rails; of my wondering, even then, why pew-openers must always be the most disagreeable females procurable, and whether there is any religious dread of a disastrous infection of good humour which renders it indispensable to set those vessels of vinegar upon the road to heaven.

Of the clergyman and clerk appearing; of a few boatmen and some other people strolling in; of an ancient mariner behind me, strongly scenting the church with rum; of the service beginning in a deep voice, and our all being very attentive.

Of Miss Lavinia, who acts as a semi-auxiliary bridesmaid, being the first to cry, and of her doing homage (as I take it) to the memory of Pidger in sobs; of Miss Clarissa applying a smelling-bottle; of Agnes taking care of Dora; of my aunt endeavouring to represent herself as a model of sternness, with tears rolling down her face; of little Dora trembling very much, and making her responses in faint whispers.

Of our kneeling down together, side by side; of Dora's trembling less and less, but always clasping Agnes by the hand; of the service being got through, quietly and gravely; of our all looking at each other in an April state of smiles and tears, when it is over; of my young wife being hysterical in the vestry, and crying for her poor papa, her dear papa.

Of her soon cheering up again, and our signing the register all round. Of my going into the gallery for Peggotty to bring *her* to sign it; of Peggotty's hugging me in a corner, and telling me she saw my own dear mother married; of its being over, and our going away.

Of my walking so proudly and lovingly down the aisle with my sweet wife upon my arm, through a mist of half-seen people, pulpits, monuments, pews, fonts, organs, and church windows, in which there flutter faint airs of association with my childish church at home, so long ago.

Of their whispering, as we pass, what a youthful couple we are, and what a pretty little wife she is. Of our all being so merry and talkative in the carriage going back. Of Sophy telling us that when she saw Traddles (whom I had intrusted with the license) asked for it, she almost fainted, having been convinced that he would contrive to lose it, or to have his pocket picked. Of Agnes laughing gaily; and of Dora being so fond of Agnes that she will not be separated from her, but still keeps her hand.

Of there being a breakfast, with abundance of things, pretty and substantial, to eat and drink, whereof I partake, as I should do in any other dream, without the least perception of their flavour! Eating and drinking, as I may say, nothing but love and marriage, and no more believing in the viands than in anything else.

Of my making a speech in the same dreamy fashion, without having an idea of what I want to say beyond such as may be comprehended in the full conviction that I haven't said it. Of our being very sociably and simply happy (always in a dream, though); and of Jip's having wedding cake, and its not agreeing with him afterward.

Of the pair of hired post-horses being ready, and of Dora's going away to change her dress. Of my aunt and Miss Clarissa remaining with us; and our walking in the garden; and my aunt, who has made quite a speech at breakfast touching Dora's aunts, being mightily amused with herself, but a little proud of it too.

Of Dora's being ready, and of Miss Lavinia's hovering about her, loath to lose the pretty toy that has given her so much pleasant occupation. Of Dora's making a long series of surprised discoveries that she has forgotten all sorts of little things; and of everybody's running everywhere to fetch them.

Of their all closing about Dora, when at last she begins to say good-bye, looking, with their bright colours and ribbons, like a bed of flowers. Of my darling being almost smothered among the flowers, and coming out, laughing and crying both together, to my jealous arms.

Of my wanting to carry Jip (who is to go along with us), and Dora's saying no, that she must carry him, or else he'll think she don't like him any more, now she is married, and will break his heart. Of our going arm in arm, and Dora stopping and looking back, and saying, "If I have ever been cross or ungrateful to anybody, don't remember it!" and bursting into tears.

Of her waving her little hand, and our going away once more. Of her once more stopping, and looking back, and hurrying to Agnes, and giving Agnes, above all the others, her last kisses and farewells.

We drive away together, and I awake from the dream. I believe it at last. It is my dear, dear little wife beside me, whom I love so well!

"Are you happy now, you foolish boy?" says Dora, "and sure you don't repent?"

From "OUR MUTUAL FRIEND"

By CHARLES DICKENS

CHERUBIC pa arose with as little noise as possible from beside majestic ma, one morning early, having a holiday before him. Pa and the lovely woman had a rather particular appointment to keep.

Yet pa and the lovely woman were not going out together. Bella was up before four, but had no bonnet on. She was waiting at the foot of the stairs — was sitting on the bottom stair, in fact — to receive pa when he came down, but her only object seemed to be to get pa well out of the house.

"Your breakfast is ready, sir," whispered Bella, after greeting him with a hug, "and all you have to do is to eat it up and drink it up, and escape. How do you feel, pa?"

"To the best of my judgment, like a housebreaker new to the business, my dear, who can't make himself quite comfortable till he is off the premises."

Bella tucked her arm in his with a merry, noiseless laugh, and they went down to the kitchen on tiptoe; she stopping on every separate stair to put the tip of her forefinger on her rosy lips, and then lay it on his lips, according to her favourite petting way of kissing pa.

"How do *you* feel, my love?" asked R. W., as she gave him his breakfast.

"I feel as if the Fortune-teller was coming true, dear pa, and the fair little man was turning out as was predicted."

"Ho! Only the fair little man?" said her father.

Bella put another of those finger-seals upon his lips, and then said, kneeling down by him as he sat at table: "Now, look here, sir! If you keep well up to the mark this day, what do you think you deserve? What did I promise you should have, if you were good, upon a certain occasion?"

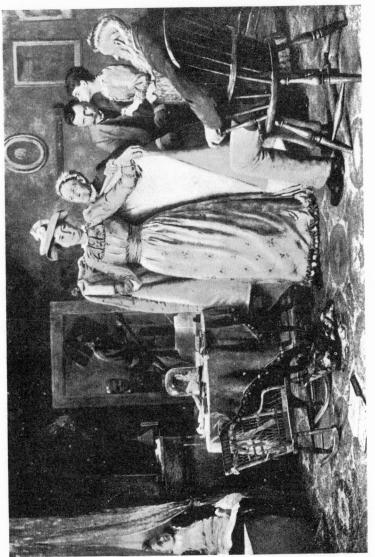

BRINGING HOME THE BRIDE.

Hovenden.

"Upon my word I don't remember, Precious. Yes, I do, though. Was n't it one of these beau—tiful tresses?" with his caressing hand upon her hair.

"Was n't it too!" returned Bella, pretending to pout. "Upon my word! Do you know, sir, that the Fortune-teller would give five thousand guineas, if it was quite convenient to him, which it is n't, for the lovely piece I have cut off for you? You can form no idea, sir, of the number of times he kissed quite a scrubby little piece — in comparison — that I cut off for *him*. And he wears it, too, round his neck, I can tell you! Near his heart!" said Bella, nodding. "Ah! very near his heart! However, you have been a good, good boy, and you are the best of all the dearest boys that ever were, this morning, and here's the chain I have made of it, pa, and you must let me put it round your neck with my own loving hands."

As pa bent his head, she cried over him a little, and then said (after having stopped to dry her eyes on his waistcoat, the discovery of which incongruous circumstance made her laugh): "Now, darling pa, give me your hands that I may fold them together, and do you say after me: My little Bella."

"My little Bella," repeated pa.

"I am fond of you."

"I am very fond of you, my darling," said pa.

"You must n't say anything not dictated to you, sir. You dare n't do it in your responses at Church, and you must n't do it in your responses out of Church."

"I withdraw the darling," said pa.

"That's a pious boy! Now again: You were always — "

"You were always," repeated pa.

"A vexatious — "

"No, you were n't," said pa.

"A vexatious (do you hear, sir?), a vexatious, capricious, thankless, troublesome Animal: but I hope you'll do better in the time to come, and I bless you and forgive you!" Here she quite forgot that it was pa's turn to make the re-

sponses, and clung to his neck. " Dear pa, if you knew
how much I think this morning of what you told me once,
about the first time of our seeing old Mr. Harmon, when
I stamped and screamed and beat you with my detestable
little bonnet ! I feel as if I had been stamping and scream-
ing and beating you with my hateful little bonnet ever since
I was born, darling ! "

" Nonsense, my love. And as to your bonnets, they
have always been nice bonnets, for they have always become — you — or you have become them ; perhaps it was
that — at every age."

" Did I hurt you much, poor little pa ? " asked Bella,
laughing (notwithstanding her repentance) with fantastic
pleasure in the picture, " when I beat you with my
bonnet ? "

" No, my child. Would n't have hurt a fly ! "

" Ay, but I am afraid I should n't have beat you at all,
unless I had meant to hurt you," said Bella. " Did I
pinch your legs, pa ? "

" Not much, my dear ; but I think it 's almost time
I — "

" Oh yes ! " cried Bella. " If I go on chattering,
you 'll be taken alive. Fly, pa, fly ! "

So they went softly up the kitchen stairs on tiptoe, and
Bella with her light hand softly removed the fastenings of
the house-door, and pa, having received a parting hug,
made off. When he had gone a little way, he looked back.
Upon which Bella set another of those finger-seals upon
the air, and thrust out her little foot expressive of the
mark. Pa, in appropriate action, expressed fidelity to the
mark, and made off as fast as he could go.

Bella walked thoughtfully in the garden for an hour and
more, and then returning to the bedroom where Lavvy the
Irrepressible still slumbered, put on a little bonnet of quiet
but on the whole of sly appearance, which she had yesterday made. " I am going for a walk, Lavvy," she said, as
she stooped down and kissed her. The Irrepressible, with
a bounce in the bed, and a remark that it was n't time to

get up yet, relapsed into unconsciousness, if she had come out of it.

Behold Bella tripping along the streets, the dearest girl afoot under the summer sun! Behold pa waiting for Bella behind a pump, at least three miles from the parental roof-tree! Behold Bella and pa aboard an early steamboat bound for Greenwich!

Were they expected at Greenwich? Probably. At least, Mr. John Rokesmith was on the pier looking out, about a couple of hours before the coaly (but to him gold-dusty) little steamboat got her steam up in London. Probably. At least, Mr. John Rokesmith seemed perfectly satisfied when he descried them on board. Probably. At least, Bella no sooner stepped ashore than she took Mr. John Rokesmith's arm, without evincing surprise, and the two walked away together with an ethereal air of happiness which, as it were, wafted up from the earth, and drew after them a gruff and glum old pensioner to see it out. Two wooden legs had this gruff and glum old pensioner, and, a minute before Bella stepped out of the boat, and drew that confiding little arm of hers through Rokesmith's, he had had no object in life but tobacco, and not enough of that. Stranded was Gruff and Glum in a harbour of everlasting mud, when all in an instant Bella floated him, and away he went.

Say, cherubic parent taking the lead, in what direction do we steer first? With some such inquiry in his thoughts, Gruff and Glum, stricken by so sudden an interest that he perked his neck and looked over the intervening people, as if he were trying to stand on tiptoe with his two wooden legs, took an observation of R. W. There was no "first" in the case, Gruff and Glum made out; the cherubic parent was bearing down and crowding on direct for Greenwich Church, to see his relations.

For Gruff and Glum, though most events acted on him simply as tobacco stoppers, pressing down and condensing the quids within him, might be imagined to trace a family resemblance between the cherubs in the church architecture and the cherub in the white waistcoat. Some remembrance of old Valentines, wherein a cherub, less appropriately attired for a proverbially uncertain climate, had been seen conducting lovers to the altar, might have been fancied to inflame the ardour of his timber toes. Be it as it might, he gave his moorings the slip, and followed in chase.

The cherub went before, all beaming smiles; Bella and John Rokesmith followed; Gruff and Glum stuck to them like wax. For years the wings of his mind had gone to look after the legs of his body; but Bella had brought them back for him per steamer, and they were spread again.

He was a slow sailer on a wind of happiness, but he took a cross cut for the rendezvous, and pegged away as if he were scoring furiously at cribbage. When the shadow of the church porch swallowed them up, victorious Gruff and Glum likewise presented himself to be swallowed up. And by this time the cherubic parent was so fearful of surprise, that, but for the two wooden legs on which Gruff and Glum was reassuringly mounted, his conscience might have introduced, in the person of that pensioner, his own stately lady disguised, arrived in Greenwich in a car and griffins, like the spiteful Fairy at the christenings of the Princesses, to do something dreadful to the marriage service. And truly he had a momentary reason to be pale of face, and to whisper to Bella, "You don't think that can be your ma; do you, my dear?" on account of a mysterious rustling and a stealthy movement somewhere in the remote neighbourhood of the organ, though it was gone directly, and was heard no more. Albeit it was heard of afterward, as will afterward be read in this veracious register of marriage.

Who taketh? I, John, and so do I, Bella. Who giveth? I, R. W. Forasmuch, Gruff and Glum, as John and Bella have consented together in holy wedlock, you may (in short) consider it done, and withdraw your two wooden legs from this temple. To the foregoing purport, the Minister speaking, as directed by the Rubric, to the People, selectly represented in the present instance by G. and G. above mentioned.

And now the church porch, having swallowed up Bella Wilfer for ever and ever, had it not in its power to relinquish that young woman, but slid into the happy sunlight Mrs. John Rokesmith instead. And long on the bright steps stood Gruff and Glum, looking after the pretty bride, with a narcotic consciousness of having dreamed a dream.

After which Bella took out from her pocket a little letter, and read it aloud to pa and John; this being a true copy of the same.

DEAREST MA, — I hope you won't be angry, but I am most happily married to Mr. John Rokesmith, who loves me better than I can ever deserve, except by loving him with all my heart. I thought it best not to mention it beforehand, in case it should cause any little difference at home. Please tell darling pa. With love to Lavvy,

Ever dearest ma,
Your affectionate daughter,
BELLA.

(P. S. Rokesmith.)

Then John Rokesmith put the queen's countenance on the letter — when had her Gracious Majesty looked so benign as on that blessed morning? — and then Bella popped it into the post-office, and said merrily, " Now, dearest pa, you are safe, and will never be taken alive! "

Pa was, at first, in the stirred depths of his conscience, so far from sure of being safe yet, that he made out majestic matrons lurking in ambush among the harmless trees of Greenwich Park, and seemed to see a stately countenance tied up in a well-known pocket-handkerchief glooming down at him from a window of the Observatory, where the Familiars of the Astronomer Royal nightly outwatch the winking stars. But, the minutes passing on, and no Mrs. Wilfer in the flesh appearing, he became more confident, and so repaired with good heart and appetite to Mr. and Mrs. John Rokesmith's cottage on Blackheath, where breakfast was ready.

A modest little cottage, but a bright and a fresh, and on the snowy table-cloth the prettiest of little breakfasts. In waiting, too, like an attendant summer breeze, a fluttering young damsel, all pink and ribbons, blushing as if she had been married instead of Bella, and yet asserting the triumph of her sex over both John and pa in an exulting and exalted flurry; as who should say, "This is what you must all come to, gentlemen, when we choose to bring you to book." This same young damsel was Bella's serving-maid, and unto her did deliver a bunch of keys, commanding treasures in the way of drysaltery, groceries, jams, and pickles, the investigation of which made pastime after breakfast, when Bella declared that "pa must taste everything, John dear, or it will never be lucky," and when pa had all sorts of things poked into his mouth, and did n't quite know what to do with them when they were put there.

Then they, all three, out for a charming ride, and for a charming stroll among heath in bloom, and there behold the identical Gruff and Glum with his wooden legs horizontally disposed before him, apparently sitting meditating on the vicissitudes of life! To whom said Bella in her light-hearted surprise: "Oh! How do you do again? What a dear old pensioner you are!" To which Gruff and Glum responded that he see her married this morning, my Beauty, and that, if it war n't a liberty, he wished her ji and the fairest of fair wind and weather; further in a general way requesting to know what cheer? and scrambling up on his two wooden legs to salute, hat in hand, ship-shape, with the gallantry of a man-of-warsman and a heart of oak.

It was a pleasant sight, in the midst of the golden bloom, to see this salt old Gruff and Glum waving his shovel hat at Bella, while his thin white hair flowed free, as if she had once more launched him into blue water again. "You are a charming old pensioner," said Bella, "and I am so happy that I wish I could make you happy too." Answered Gruff and Glum, "Give me leave to kiss your hand, my Lovely, and it 's done!" So it was done to the general contentment; and if Gruff and Glum did n't in the course of the afternoon splice the main brace, it was not for want of the means of inflicting that outrage on the feelings of the Infant Bands of Hope.

But the marriage dinner was the crowning success, for what had bride and bridegroom plotted to do, but to have and to hold that dinner in the very room of the very hotel where pa and the lovely woman had once dined together! Bella sat between pa and John, and divided her attentions pretty equally, but felt it necessary (in the waiter's absence before dinner) to remind pa that she was *his* lovely woman no longer.

" I am well aware of it, my dear," returned the cherub, " and I resign you willingly."

" Willingly, sir? You ought to be broken-hearted."

" So I should be, my dear, if I thought that I was going to lose you."

" But you know you are not; don't you, poor dear pa? You know that you have only made a new relation who will be as fond of you and as thankful to you — for my sake and your own sake both — as I am; don't you, dear little pa? Look here, pa!" Bella put her finger on her own lip, and then on pa's, and then on her own lip again, and then on her husband's.

" Now we are a partnership of three, dear pa."

The appearance of dinner here cut Bella short in one of her disappearances: the more effectually, because it was put on under the auspices of a solemn gentleman in black clothes and a white cravat, who looked much more like a clergyman than *the* clergyman, and seemed to have mounted a great deal higher in the church; not to say scaled the steeple. This dignitary, conferring in secrecy with John Rokesmith on the subject of punch and wines, bent his head as though stooping to the Papistical practice of receiving auricular confession. Likewise, on John's offering a suggestion which did n't meet his views, his face became overcast and reproachful, as enjoining penance.

What a dinner! Specimens of all the fishes that swim

in the sea surely had swum their way to it, and if samples
of the fishes of divers colours that made a speech in the
Arabian Nights (quite a ministerial explanation in respect
of cloudiness), and then jumped out of the frying-pan,
were not to be recognised, it was only because they had
all become of one hue by being cooked in batter among the
whitebait. And the dishes being seasoned with Bliss —
an article which they are sometimes out of at Greenwich
— were of perfect flavour, and the golden drinks had been
bottled in the golden ages and hoarding up their sparkles
ever since.

The best of it was, that Bella and John and the cherub
had made a covenant that they would not reveal to mortal
eyes any appearance whatever of being a wedding party.
Now, the supervising dignitary, the Archbishop of Greenwich, knew this as well as if he had performed the nuptial
ceremony. And the loftiness with which his Grace entered
into their confidence without being invited, and insisted on
a show of keeping the waiters out of it, was the crowning
glory of the entertainment.

There was an innocent young waiter of a slender form
and with weakish legs, as yet unversed in the wiles of
waiterhood, and but too evidently of a romantic temperament, and deeply (if it were not too much to add, hopelessly)
in love with some young female not aware of his merit.
This guileless youth, descrying the position of affairs, which
even his innocence could not mistake, limited his waiting
to languishing admiringly against the sideboard when Bella
did n't want anything, and swooping at her when she did.
Him his Grace the Archbishop perpetually obstructed, cutting him out with his elbow in the moment of success, dis-
patching him in degrading quest of melted butter, and when,
by any chance, he got hold of any dish worth having,
bereaving him of it, and ordered him to stand back.

" Pray excuse him, madam," said the Archbishop, in a low
stately voice; " he is a very young man on liking, and we
don't like him."

This induced John Rokesmith to observe — by way of

making the thing more natural — " Bella, my love, this is so much more successful than any of our past anniversaries, that I think we must keep our future anniversaries here."

Whereunto Bella replied, with probably the least successful attempt at looking matronly that ever was seen: " Indeed, I think so, John dear."

Here the Archbishop of Greenwich coughed a stately cough to attract the attention of three of his ministers present, and, staring at them, seemed to say, " I call upon you by your fealty to believe this!"

With his own hands he afterward put on the dessert, as remarking to the three guests, " The period has now arrived at which we can dispense with the assistance of those fellows who are not in our confidence," and would have retired with complete dignity but for a daring action issuing from the misguided brain of the young man on liking. He finding, by ill-fortune, a piece of orange flower somewhere in the lobbies, now approached undetected with the same in a finger-glass, and placed it on Bella's right hand. The Archbishop instantly ejected and excommunicated him; but the thing was done.

" I trust, madam," said his Grace, returning alone, " that you will have the kindness to overlook it, in consideration of its being the act of a very young man who is merely here on liking, and who will never answer."

With that he solemnly bowed and retired, and they all burst into laughter, long and merry. " Disguise is of no use," said Bella; " they all find me out; I think it must be, pa and John dear, because I look so happy!"

Her husband feeling it necessary at this point to demand one of those mysterious disappearances on Bella's part, she dutifully obeyed; saying, in a softened voice from her place of concealment, —

" You remember how we talked about the ships that day, pa?"

" Yes, my dear."

" Isn't it strange, now, to think that there was no John in all the ships, pa?"

" Not at all, my dear."

" Oh, pa! Not at all?"

" No, my dear. How can we tell what coming people are aboard the ships that may be sailing to us now from the unknown seas?"

Bella remaining invisible and silent, her father remained at his dessert and wine until he remembered it was time for him to get home to Holloway. " Though I positively cannot tear myself away," he cherubically added — " it would be a sin — without drinking to many, many happy returns of this most happy day."

" Hear! ten thousand times!" cried John. " I fill my glass and my precious wife's."

" Gentlemen," said the cherub, inaudibly addressing, in his Anglo-Saxon tendency to throw his feelings into the form of a speech, the boys down below, who were bidding against each other to put their heads in the mud for sixpence: " Gentlemen — and Bella and John — you will readily suppose that it is not my intention to trouble you with many observations on the present occasion. You will also at once infer the nature and even the terms of the toast I am about to propose on the present occasion. Gentlemen — and Bella and John — the present occasion is an occasion fraught with feelings that I cannot trust myself to express. But, gentlemen — and Bella and John — for the part I have had in it, for the confidence you have placed in me, and for the affectionate good-nature and kindness with which you have determined not to find me in the way, when I am well aware that I cannot be otherwise than in it more or less, I do most heartily thank you. Gentlemen — and Bella and John — my love to you, and may we meet, as on the present occasion, on many future occasions; that is to say, gentlemen — and Bella and John — on many happy returns of the present happy occasion."

Having thus concluded his address, the amiable cherub embraced his daughter, and took his flight to the steamboat which was to convey him to London, and was then lying at the floating pier, doing its best to bump the same to bits.

But the happy couple were not going to part with him in that way, and, before he had been on board two minutes, there they were, looking down at him from the wharf above.

" Pa dear ! " cried Bella, beckoning him with her parasol to approach the side, and bending gracefully to whisper.

" Yes, my darling."

" Did I beat you much with that horrid little bonnet, pa ? "

" Nothing to speak of, my dear."

" Did I pinch your legs, pa ? "

" Only nicely, my pet."

" You are sure you quite forgive me, pa ? Please, pa, please, forgive me quite ! " Half laughing at him and half crying to him, Bella besought him with the prettiest manner; in a manner so engaging and so playful and so natural that her cherubic parent made a coaxing face as if she had never grown up, and said, " What a silly little Mouse it is ! "

" But you do forgive me that, and everything else; don't you, pa ? "

" Yes, my dearest."

" And you don't feel solitary or neglected, going away by yourself; do you, pa ? "

" Lord bless you ! No, my Life ! "

" Good-bye, dearest pa. Good-bye ! "

" Good-bye, my darling ! Take her away, my dear John. Take her home ! "

So, she leaning on her husband's arm, they turned homeward by a rosy path which the gracious sun struck out for them in its setting. And oh ! there are days in this life worth life and worth death. And oh, what a bright old song it is, that Oh, 't is love, 't is love, 't is love, that makes the world go round !

"LIKE A LAVEROCK IN THE LIFT"

By JEAN INGELOW

IT 's we two, it 's we two for aye,
   All the world, and we two, and Heaven be our stay!
Like a laverock in the lift, sing, O bonny bride!
All the world was Adam once, with Eve by his side.

What 's the world, my lass, my love! — what can it do?
I am thine, and thou art mine; life is sweet and new.
If the world have missed the mark, let it stand by;
For we two have gotten leave, and once more will try.

Like a laverock in the lift, sing, O bonny bride!
It 's we two, it 's we two, happy side by side.
Take a kiss from me, thy man; now the song begins;
"All is made afresh for us, and the brave heart wins."

When the darker days come, and no sun will shine,
Thou shalt dry my tears, my lass, and I 'll dry thine.
It 's we two, it 's we two, while the world 's away,
Sitting by the golden sheaves on our wedding day.

Sevenoaks

From "SEVENOAKS"[1]

By J. G. HOLLAND

THERE was a great commotion in the little Sevenoaks tavern. It was Jim's wedding morning, and
on the previous evening there had been a sufficient number of arrivals to fill every room. Mr. and Mrs. Balfour,
with the two boys, had come in by the evening stage;
Jim and Mr. Benedict had arrived from Number Nine.
Friends of Miss Butterworth from adjoining towns had
come, so as to be ready for the ceremony of the morning.
Villagers had thronged the noisy bar-room until midnight,
scanning and discussing the strangers and speculating upon
the event which had called them together. Jim had
moved among them smiling, and returning their good-
natured badinage with imperturbable coolness, so far as
appearances went, though he acknowledged to Mr. Balfour that he felt very much as he did about his first moose.

"I took a good aim," said he, "restin' acrost a stump,
but the stump was oneasy like; an' then I blazed away,
an' when I observed the moose sprawlin', I was twenty
feet up a tree, with my gun in the snow; an' if they don't
find me settin' on the parson's chimbly about nine o'clock
to-morrer mornin', it won't be on account o' my not bein'
skeered."

But the wedding morning had arrived. Jim had had an
uneasy night, with imperfect sleep and preposterous dreams.
He had been pursuing game. Sometimes it was a bear
that attracted his chase, sometimes it was a moose, but
all the time it was Miss Butterworth, flying and looking
back, with robes and ribbons vanishing among the distant
trees, until he shot and killed her, and then he woke in a

[1] *By permission of Charles Scribner's Sons, from "Sevenoaks," by J. G.
Holland. Copyright by Scribner, Armstrong & Co.,1875. Copyright by Charles
Scribner's Sons, 1882.*

great convulsion of despair, to hear the singing of the early birds and to the realisation of the fact that his days of bachelor life were counted.

Mr. Benedict, with his restored boy in his arms, occupied the room next to his, a door opening between them. Both were awake, and were busy with their whispered confidences, when they became aware that Jim was roused and on his feet. In a huge bundle on the table lay Jim's wedding garments, which he eyed from time to time as he busied himself at his bath.

"Won't ye be a purty bird with them feathers on! This makin' crows into bobolinks 'll do for oncet, but, my! won't them things spin when I git into the woods agin?"

Benedict and Harry knew Jim's habit and the measure of excitement that was upon him, and lay still, expecting to be amused by his soliloquies. Soon they heard him say, —

"Oh, lay down, lay down, lay *down*, ye misable old mop!"

It was an expression of impatience and disgust.

"What's the matter, Jim?" Mr. Benedict called.

"Here's my har," responded Jim, "actin' as if it was a piece of woods or a haylot, an' there ain't no lodgin' it with nothin' short of a harricane. I've a good mind to git it shingled and san'-papered."

Then shifting his address to the object of his care and anxiety, he went on, —

"Oh, stick up, stick up, if you want to! Don't lay down on my 'count. P'r'aps you want to see what's goin' on. P'r'aps ye 're goin' to stand up with me. P'r'aps ye want to skeer somebody's hosses. If I did n't look no better nor you, I sh'd want to lay low; an' if I 'd 'a' slep' as poor as ye did last night, I 'd lop down in the first bed o' bear's grease I could find. *Hain't* ye got no manners?"

This was too much for Harry, who, in his happy mood, burst into the merriest laughter.

This furnished Jim with just the apology he wanted for

HEALTH TO THE BRIDE.

a frolic, and rushing into the adjoining bedroom, he pulled Harry from his bed, seated him on the top of his head, and marched with him struggling and laughing about the room. After he had performed sundry acrobatic feats with him, he carried him back to his bed. Then he returned to his room, and entered seriously upon the task of arraying himself in his wedding attire. To get on his collar and necktie properly, he was obliged to call for Mr. Benedict's assistance.

Jim was already getting red in the face.

"What on earth folks want to tie theirselves up in this way for in hot weather is more nor I know," he said. "How do ye s'pose them Mormons live, as is doin' this every three days?"

Jim asked this question with his nose in the air, patiently waiting the result of Mr. Benedict's manipulations at his throat. When he could speak again he added, —

"I vow, if I was doin' a big business in this line I'd git some tin things, an' have 'em soddered on, an' sleep in 'em."

This sent Harry into another giggle, and, with many soliloquies and much merriment, the dressing in both rooms went on, until in Jim's room all became still. When Benedict and his boy had completed their toilet, they looked in upon Jim, and found him dressed and seated upon his trunk.

"Good-morning, Mr. Fenton," said Benedict, cheerfully.

Jim, who had been in deep thought, looked up, and said, —

"Do ye know that that don't seem so queer to me as it used to? It seems all right fur pertickler friends to call me Jim, but clo'es is what puts the Mister into a man. I felt it comin' when I looked into the glass. . . . I never knowed exactly where the Mister come from afore. Ye have to be measured fo't. A pair o' shears, an' a needle an' thread, an' a hot goose is what changes a man into Mister. It's a nice thing to find out, but it's uncomf'table."

How long Jim would have indulged in his philosophy of the power of dress had he not been disturbed will never be known, for at this moment Mr. Balfour knocked at his door and was admitted. Sam Yates followed, and both looked Jim over and pronounced him perfect. Even these familiar friends felt the power of dress, and treated Jim in a way to which he had been unaccustomed. The stalwart figure, developed in every muscle, and becomingly draped, was well calculated to excite their admiration. The refractory hair, which had given its possessor so much trouble, simply made his head impressive and picturesque. There was a man before them — humane, brave, bright, original. All he wanted was culture. Physical and mental endowments were in excess, and the two men trained in the schools had learned to love — almost to revere him. Until he spoke, they did not feel at home with him in his new disguise.

They all descended to breakfast together. Jim was quiet under the feeling that his clothes were an unnatural expression of himself, and that his words would make them a mockery. He was awed, too, by the presence of Mrs. Balfour, who met him at the table for the first time in her life. The sharp-eyed Yankee girls who waited at the meal were very much devoted to Jim, who was ashamed to receive so much attention. On the whole, it was the most uncomfortable breakfast he had ever eaten; but his eyes were quick to see all that was done, for he was about to open a hotel, and wished particularly to learn the details of the table service.

There was great excitement, too, at the parsonage that morning. The Misses Snow were stirred by the romance of the occasion. They had little enough of this element in their lives, and were disposed to make the most of it when it came. The eldest had been invited to accompany the bride to Number Nine, and spend a few weeks with her there. As this was accounted a great privilege by the two younger sisters, they quietly shelved her, and told her that they were to have their own way at home; so Miss Snow became ornamental and critical. Miss Butterworth had spent the night with her, and they talked like a pair of school-girls until the small hours of the morning. The two younger girls had slept together, and discussed at length the duties of their respective offices. One was to do the bride's hair and act as the general supervisor of her dress, the other was to arrange the flowers and take care of the guests. Miss Butterworth's hair was not beautiful, and how it was to be made the most of, was the great question that agitated the hair-dresser. All the possibilities of braid and plait and curl were canvassed. If she only had a switch, a great triumph could be achieved; but she had none, and, what was worse, would have none. A neighbour had sent in a potted white rose, full of buds and bloom, and over this the sisters quarrelled. The hair would not be complete without the roses, and the table would look " shameful " if the pot did not stand upon it unshorn of a charm. The hair-dresser proposed that the stems which she was bent on despoiling should have some artificial roses tied to them, but the disgraceful project was rejected with scorn. They wrangled over the dear little rose-bush and its burden until they went to sleep, — one to dream that Miss Butterworth had risen in the morning with a new head of hair that reached to her knee, in whose luxuriance she could revel with interminable delight; and the other that the house was filled with roses, — that they sprouted out of the walls, fluttered with beads of dew against the windows, strewed the floor and filled the air with odour.

Miss Butterworth was not to step out of the room — not to be seen by any mortal eye — until she should come forth as a bride. Miss Snow was summarily expelled from the apartment, and only permitted to bring in Miss Butterworth's breakfast, while her self-appointed lady's-maid did her hair, and draped her in her new gray silk.

" Make just as big a fool of me, my dear, as you choose," said the prospective bride to the fussy little girl who fluttered about her. " It's only for a day and I don't care."

Such patient manipulation, such sudden retiring for the study of effects, such delicious little experiments with a curl, such shifting of hairpins, such dainty adjustments of ruffles and frills as were indulged in in that little room, can only be imagined by the sex familiar with them. And then, in the midst of it all, came a scream of delight that stopped everything. Mrs. Balfour had sent in a great box full of the most exquisite flowers, which she had brought all the way from the city. The youngest Miss Snow was wild with her new wealth, and there were roses for Miss Butterworth's hair, and her throat, and a bouquet for her hand. And after this came wonderful accessions to the refreshment table. Cake, with Miss Butterworth's initials; tarts, marked "Number Nine," and Charlotte de Russe, with a "B" and an "F" hopelessly twisted together in a monogram. The most excited exclamations reached Miss Butterworth's ears in her imprisonment, —

"Goodness, gracious me!"

"If there is n't another cake as big as a flour-barrel!"

"Tell your mother she's an angel. She's coming down to help us eat it, I hope."

"Just look at this basket of little cakes! I was saying to mother this minute that that was all we wanted."

So the good things came, and the cheerful givers went, and Miss Butterworth took an occasional sip at her coffee, with a huge napkin at her throat, and tears in her eyes, not drawn forth by the delicate tortures in progress upon her person. She thought of her weary years of service, her watchings by sick-beds, her ministry to the poor, her long loneliness, and acknowledged to herself that her reward had come. To be so loved and petted and cared for and waited upon, was payment for every sacrifice and every service, and she felt that she and the world were at quits.

Before the finishing touches to her toilet were given, there was a tumult at the door. She could hear new voices. The guests were arriving. She heard laughter and merry greetings; and still they poured in, as if they had come in a procession. Then there was a hush, followed by the sound of a carriage, the letting down of steps, and a universal murmur. Jim had arrived, with Mr. and Mrs. Balfour and the boys. They had had great difficulty in getting him into the one hackney coach which the village possessed, on account of his wish to ride with the driver, "a feller as he knowed;" but he was overruled by Mrs. Balfour, who, on alighting, took his arm. He came up the garden walk, smiling in the faces and eyes of those gathered about the door and clustered at the windows. In his wedding dress he was the best figure in the crowd, and many were the exclamations of feminine admiration.

On entering the door, he looked about him, saw the well-dressed and expectant company, the dainty baskets of flowers, the bountifully loaded table in the little dining-room, all the preparations for his day of happiness, but he saw nowhere the person who gave to him the significance of the occasion.

Mr. Snow greeted him cordially, and introduced him to those who stood near.

"Well, parson, where's the little woman?" he said, at last, in a voice so loud that all heard the startling question. Miss Butterworth heard him and laughed.

"Just hear him!" she exclaimed to the busy girl, whose work was now hurrying to a close. "If he does n't aston-ish them before he gets through, I shall be mistaken. I do think it's the most ridiculous thing. Now, is n't it! The idea."

Miss Snow, in the general character of outside manager and future companion of the bride, hurried to Jim's side at once and said, —

"Oh, Mr. Fenton!"

"Jest call me Jim."

"No, no, I won't. Now, Mr. Fenton, really! you can't see her until she is ready."

"Oh, can't I!" and Jim smiled.

Miss Snow had the impression, prevalent among women, that a bridegroom has no rights so long as they can keep him out of them, and that it is their privilege to fight him up to the last moment.

"Now, really, Mr. Fenton, you *must* be patient," she said in a whisper. "She is quite delicate this morning, and she's going to look so pretty that you'll hardly know her."

"Well," said Jim, "if you've got a ticket into the place whar she's stoppin', tell her that kingdom-come is here an' waitin'."

A ripple of laughter went round the circle, and Jim, finding the room getting a little close, beckoned Mr. Snow out of doors. Taking him aside and removing his hat, he said, —

"Parson, do you see my har?"

"I do," responded the minister, good-naturedly.

"That riz last night," said Jim, solemnly.

"Is it possible?" and Mr. Snow looked at the intractable pile with genuine concern.

"Yes, riz in a dream. I thought I'd shot 'er. I was follerin' 'er all night. Sometimes she was one thing and sometimes she was another, but I drew a bead on 'er an' down she went, an' up come my har quicker nor lightnin'. I don't s'pose it looks very purty, but I can't help it."

"Have you tried anything on it?" inquired Mr. Snow, with a puzzled look.

"Yis, everything but a hot flat-iron, an' I'm a little afraid o' that. If wust comes to wust, it'll have to be did, though. It may warm up my old brains a little, but if my har is well sprinkled an' the thing is handled lively, it'll pay for tryin'."

The perfect candour and coolness of Jim's manner were too much for the unsuspicious spirit of the minister, who thought it all very strange. He had heard of such things, but this was the first instance he had ever seen.

"Parson," said Jim, changing the topic, "what's the damage for the sort o' thing ye're drivin' at this mornin'?"

"The what?"

" The damage — what's the — well — damage? What do ye consider a fa'r price? "

" Do you mean the marriage fee? "

" Yes, I guess that's what ye call it."

" The law allows us two dollars, but you will allow me to perform the ceremony for nothing. It's a labour of love, Mr. Fenton. We are all very much interested in Miss Butterworth, as you see."

" Well, I'm a little interested in 'er myself, an' I'm goin' to pay for the splice. Jest tuck that X into yer jacket, an' tell yer neighbours as ye've seen a man as was five times better nor the law."

" You are very generous."

" No; I know what business is, though. Ye have to get somethin' to square the buryin's and baptisin's with. When a man has a weddin', he'd better pay the whole thing in a lump. Parsons have to live, but how the devil they do it in Sevenoaks is more nor I know."

" Mr. Fenton, excuse me! " said Mr. Snow, colouring, " but I am not accustomed to hearing language of that kind."

" No, I s'pose not," said Jim, who saw too late that he had made a mistake. " You sort o' folks knuckle to the devil more nor I do. A good bein' I take to, but a bad bein' I'm careless with; an' I don't make no more o' slingin' his name round nor I do kickin' an old boot."

Mr. Snow was obliged to laugh, and half a dozen others, who had gathered about them, joined in a merry chorus.

Then Miss Snow came out and whispered to her father and gave a roguish glance at Jim. At this time the house was full, and the little yard was full, and there was a crowd of boys at the gate. Mr. Snow took Jim by the arm and led him in. They pressed through the crowd at the door, Miss Snow making way for them, and so, in a sort of triumphal progress, they went through the room, and disappeared in the apartment where the " little woman," flushed and expectant, waited their arrival.

It would be hard to tell which was the more surprised

31

as they were confronted by the meeting. Dress had wrought its miracle upon both of them, and they hardly knew each other.

"Well, little woman, how fare ye?" said Jim; and he advanced, and took her cheeks tenderly between his rough hands and kissed her.

"Oh, don't! Mr. Fenton! You'll muss her hair!" exclaimed the nervous little lady's-maid of the morning, dancing about the object of her delightful toils and anxieties, and readjusting a rose, and pulling out the fold of a ruffle.

"A purty job ye've made on't! The little woman'll never look so nice again," said Jim.

"Perhaps I shall — when I'm married again," said Miss Butterworth, looking up into Jim's eyes and laughing.

"Now, ain't that sassy!" exclaimed Jim, in a burst of admiration. "That's what took me the first time I seen 'er."

Then Miss Snow Number Two came in, and said it really was time for the ceremony to begin. Such a job as she had had in seating people!

Oh, the mysteries of that little room! How the people outside wondered what was going on there! How the girls inside rejoiced in their official privileges!

Miss Snow took Jim by the button-hole,—

"Mr. Fenton, you must take Miss Butterworth on your arm, you know, and lead her in front of the sofa, and turn around and face father, and then do just what he tells you, and remember that there's nothing for you to say."

The truth was, they were all afraid that Jim would not be able to hold his tongue.

"Are we all ready?" inquired Mr. Snow, in a pleasant official tone.

All were ready; and then Mr. Snow, going out with a book in his hand, was followed by Jim and his bride, the little procession being completed by the three Misses Snow, who, with a great deal of care upon their faces, slipped out of the door, one after another, like three white doves from a window. Mr. Snow took his position, the pair wheeled and faced him, and the three Misses Snow supported Miss Butterworth as impromptu bridesmaids. It was an impressive tableau, and when the good pastor said, " Let us pray," and raised his white hands, a painter in search of a subject could have asked for nothing better.

When, at the close of his prayer, the pastor inquired if there were any known obstacles to the union of the pair before him in the bonds of holy matrimony, and bade all objectors to speak then, or for ever after hold their peace, Jim looked around with a defiant air, as if he would like to see the man who would respond to the cail. No one did respond, and the ceremony proceeded.

" James," said Mr. Snow.

" Jest call me — "

Miss Butterworth pinched Jim's arm, and he recalled Miss Snow's injunction in time to arrest his sentence in mid-passage.

" James," the pastor repeated, and then went on to ask him, in accordance with the simple form of his sect, whether he took the woman whom he was holding by the hand to be his lawful and wedded wife, to be loved and cherished in sickness and health, in prosperity and adversity, cleaving to her, and to her only.

" Parson," said Jim, " that's jest what I'm here for."

There would have been a titter if any other man had said it, but it was so strong and earnest, and so much in character, that hardly a smile crossed a face that fronted him.

The " Keziah " was questioned in the usual form, and bowed her response, and Jim and the little woman were declared to be one. " What God hath joined together, let not man put asunder."

And then Mr. Snow raised his white hands again, and pronounced a formal benediction. There was a moment of awkwardness, but soon the pastor advanced with his congratulations, and Mrs. Snow came up, and the three Misses Snow, and the Balfours and the neighbours ; and there were kisses and hand-shakings and good wishes.

Jim beamed around upon the fluttering and chattering group like a great, good-natured mastiff upon a playful collection of silken spaniels and smart terriers. It was the proudest moment of his life. Even when standing on the cupola of his hotel, surveying his achievements and counting his possessions, he had never felt the thrill which moved him then. The little woman was his, and his for ever. His manhood had received the highest public recognition, and he was as happy as if it had been the imposition of a crown.

"Ye made purty solemn business on 't, Parson," said Jim.

"It's a very important step, Mr. Fenton," responded the clergyman.

"Step!" exclaimed Jim. "That's no name for 't; it's a whole trip. But I sh'll do it. When I said it I meaned it. I sh'll take care o' the little woman, an' atween you an' I, Parson, it's about the best thing as a man can do. Takin' care of a woman is the nateral thing for a man, an' no man ain't much as does n't do it, an' glad o' the job."

The capacity of a country assembly for cakes, pies, and lemonade is something quite unique, especially at a morning festival. If the table groaned at the beginning, it sighed at the close. The abundance that asserted itself in piles of dainties was left a wreck. It faded away like a bank of snow before a drift of southern vapour. Jim, foraging among the solids, found a mince-pie, to which he devoted himself.

"This is the sort o' thing as will stan' by a man in trouble," said he, with a huge piece in his hand.

Then, with a basket of cake, he vanished from the house, and distributed his burden among the boys at the gate.

"Boys, I know ye 're hungry, 'cause ye 've left yer breakfast on yer faces. Now git this in afore it rains."

The boys did not stand on the order of the service, but helped themselves greedily, and left his basket empty in a twinkling.

" It beats all nater," said Jim, looking at them sym-
pathetically, " how much boys can put down when they
try. If the facks could be knowed without cuttin' into
'em, I 'd be willin' to bet somethin' that their legs is holler."

While Jim was absent, the bride's health was drunk in
a glass of lemonade, and when he returned, his own health
was proposed, and Jim seemed to feel that something was
expected of him.

" My good frens," said he, " I 'm much obleeged to ye.
Ye could n't 'a' treated me better if I 'd 'a' been President
of this country. I ain't used to yer ways, but I know
when I 'm treated well an' when the little woman is treated
well. I 'm obleeged to yer on her 'count. I 'm a-goin'
to take 'er into the woods, an' take care on 'er. We are
goin' to keep a hotel — me an' the little woman — an' if
so be as any of ye is took sick by overloadin' with cookies
'arly in the day, or bein' thinned out with lemonade, ye
can come into the woods, an' I 'll send ye back happy."

There was a clapping of hands and a fluttering of handkerchiefs and a merry chorus of laughter, and then two
vehicles drove up to the door. The bride bade a tearful
farewell to her multitude of friends, and poured out her
thanks to the minister's family, and in twenty minutes
thereafter two happy loads of passengers went pounding
over the bridge, and off up the hill on the way to Number
Nine. The horses were strong, the morning was perfect,
and Jim was in possession of his bride. They, with Miss
Snow, occupied one carriage, while Mr. Benedict and the
Balfours filled the other. Not a member of the company
started homeward until the bridal party was seen climbing
the hill in the distance, but waited, commenting upon the
great event of the morning, and speculating upon the future
of the pair whose marriage they had witnessed. There
was not a woman in the crowd who did not believe in Jim;
and all were glad that the little tailoress had reached so
pleasant and stimulating a change in her life.

When the voyagers had passed beyond the scattered
farmhouses into the lonely country, Jim, with his wife's

help, released himself from the collar and cravat that tormented him and once more breathed freely. On they sped, shouting to one another from carriage to carriage, and Mike Conlin's humble house was reached in a two hours' drive. There was chaffing at the door and romping among the trees while the horses were refreshed, and then they pushed on again with such speed as was possible with poorer roads and soberer horses; and two hours before sunset they were at the river. The little woman had enjoyed the drive. When she found that she had cut loose from her old life, and was entering upon one unknown and untried, in pleasant companionship, she was thoroughly happy. It was all like a fairy story; and there before her rolled the beautiful river, and, waiting on the shore, were the trunks and remnants of baggage that had been started for their destination before daylight, and the guides with their boats, and with wild-flowers in their hat-bands. The carriages were dismissed to find their way back to Mike Conlin's that night, while Jim, throwing off his coat, assisted in loading the three boats. Mr. Balfour had brought along with him, not only a large flag for the hotel, but half a dozen smaller ones for the little fleet. The flags were soon mounted upon little rods, and set up at either end of each boat, and when the luggage was all loaded, and the passengers had taken their places — Jim taking his wife and Miss Snow in his own familiar craft — they pushed out into the stream, and started for a race. Jim was the most powerful man of the three, and was aching for work. It was a race all the way, but the broader chest and harder muscles won. It was a regatta without spectators, but as full of excitement as if the shores had been fringed with a cheering crowd.

The two women chatted together in the stern of Jim's boat, or sat in silence, as if they were enchanted, watching the changing shores, while the great shadows of the woods deepened upon them. They had never seen anything like it. It was a new world — God's world, which man had not marred.

At last they heard the barking of a dog, and, looking far up among the woods, they caught the vision of a new building. The boys in the boats behind yelled with delight. Ample in its dimensions and fair in its outlines, there stood the little woman's home. Her eyes filled with tears, and she hid them on Miss Snow's shoulder.

" Be ye disap'inted, little woman ? " inquired Jim, tenderly.

" Oh, no."

" Feelin's a little too many fur ye ? "

The little woman nodded, while Miss Snow put her arm around her neck and whispered.

" A woman is a curi's bein'," said Jim. " She cries when she 's tickled an' she laughs when she 's mad."

" I 'm not mad," said the little woman, bursting into a laugh and lifting her tear-burdened eyes to Jim.

" An' then," said Jim, " she cries and laughs all to oncet, an' a feller don't know whether to take off his jacket or put up his umberell."

This quite restored the " little woman," and her eyes were dry and merry as the boat touched the bank, and the two women were helped ashore. Before the other boats came up, they were in the house, with the delighted Turk at their heels, and Mike Conlin's wife courtesying before them.

It was a merry night at Number Nine. Jim's wife became the mistress at once. She knew where everything was to be found, as well as if she had been there for a year, and played the hostess to Mr. and Mrs. Balfour as agreeably as if her life had been devoted to the duties of her establishment.

From "THE COURTSHIP OF MILES STANDISH"[1]

By HENRY WADSWORTH LONGFELLOW

THIS was the wedding morn of Priscilla the Puritan maiden.
Friends were assembled together; the Elder and Magistrate also
Graced the scene with their presence, and stood like the Law and the Gospel,
One with the sanction of earth, and one with the blessing of heaven.
Simple and brief was the wedding, as that of Ruth and of Boaz.
Softly the youth and the maiden repeated the words of betrothal,
Taking each other for husband and wife in the Magistrate's presence,
After the Puritan way, and the laudable custom of Holland.
Fervently then and devoutly, the excellent Elder of Plymouth
Prayed for the hearth and the home, that were founded that day in affection,
Speaking of life and of death, and imploring Divine benedictions.

Lo! when the service was ended, a form appeared on the threshold,
Clad in armour of steel, a sombre and sorrowful figure!
Why does the bridegroom start and stare at the strange apparition?
Why does the bride turn pale, and hide her face on his shoulder?

---

[1] *By special permission of Houghton, Mifflin & Co.*

THE MARRIAGE OF POCAHONTAS.
Brueckner.

Is it a phantom of air, — a bodiless, spectral illusion?
Is it a ghost from the grave, that has come to forbid the
  betrothal?
Long had it stood there unseen, a guest uninvited,
  unwelcomed;
Over its clouded eyes there had passed at times an expression
Softening the gloom and revealing the warm heart hidden
  beneath them,
As when across the sky the driving rack of the rain cloud
Grows for a moment thin, and betrays the sun by its
  brightness.
Once it had lifted its hand, and moved its lips, but was
  silent,
As if an iron will had mastered the fleeting intention.
But when were ended the troth and the prayer and the last
  benediction,
Into the room it strode, and the people beheld with
  amazement
Bodily there in his armour Miles Standish, the Captain of
  Plymouth.
Grasping the bridegroom's hand, he said with emotion,
  "Forgive me!
I have been angry and hurt, — too long have I cherished
  the feeling.
I have been cruel and hard, but now, thank God! it is
  ended.
Mine is the same hot blood that leaped in the veins of
  Hugh Standish,
Sensitive, swift to resent, but as swift in atoning for error.
Never so much as now was Miles Standish the friend of
  John Alden."
Thereupon answered the bridegroom: "Let all be forgotten
  between us, —
All save the dear old friendship, and that shall grow older
  and dearer!"
Then the Captain advanced, and, bowing, saluted Priscilla,
Gravely, and after the manner of old-fashioned gentry in
  England,

Something of camp and of court, of town and of country,
    commingled,
Wishing her joy of her wedding, and loudly lauding her
    husband.
Then he said with a smile: " I should have remembered
    the adage, —
If you would be well served, you must serve yourself; and
    moreover,
No man can gather cherries in Kent at the season of
    Christmas ! "

Great was the people's amazement, and greater yet their
    rejoicing,
Thus to behold once more the sunburnt face of their
    Captain,
Whom they had mourned as dead; and they gathered and
    crowded about him,
Eager to see him and hear him, forgetful of bride and of
    bridegroom,
Questioning, answering, laughing, and each interrupting the
    other,
Till the good Captain declared, being quite overpowered
    and bewildered,
He had rather by far break into an Indian encampment
Than come again to a wedding to which he had not been
    invited.

Meanwhile the bridegroom went forth and stood with the
    bride at the doorway,
Breathing the perfumed air of that warm and beautiful
    morning.
Touched with autumnal tints, but lonely and sad in the
    sunshine,
Lay extended before them the land of toil and privation ;
There were the graves of the dead, and the barren waste of
    the seashore,
There the familiar fields, the groves of pine, and the
    meadows ;

But to their eyes transfigured, it seemed as the Garden of
    Eden,
Filled with the presence of God, whose voice was the sound
    of the ocean.

Soon was their vision disturbed by the noise and stir of
    departure,
Friends coming forth from the house, and impatient of
    longer delaying,
Each with his plan for the day, and the work that was left
    uncompleted.
Then from a stall near at hand, amid exclamations of
    wonder,
Alden, the thoughtful, the careful, so happy, so proud of
    Priscilla,
Brought out his snow-white bull, obeying the hand of its
    master.
Led by a cord that was tied to an iron ring in its nostrils,
Covered with crimson cloth, and a cushion placed for a
    saddle.
She should not walk, he said, through the dust and heat of
    the noonday ;
Nay, she should ride like a queen, not plod along like a
    peasant.
Somewhat alarmed at first, but reassured by the others,
Placing her hand on the cushion, her foot in the hand of
    her husband,
Gaily, with joyous laugh, Priscilla mounted her palfrey.
" Nothing is wanting now," he said with a smile, " but
    the distaff ;
Then you would be in truth my queen, my beautiful
    Bertha ! "

Onward the bridal procession now moved to their new
    habitation,
Happy husband and wife, and friends conversing together.
Pleasantly murmured the brook, as they crossed the ford in
    the forest,

Pleased with the image that passed, like a dream of love
  through its bosom,
Tremulous, floating in air, o'er the depths of the azure
  abysses.
Down through the golden leaves the sun was pouring his
  splendours,
Gleaming on purple grapes, that, from branches above them
  suspended
Mingled their odorous breath with the balm of the pine and
  the fir-tree,
Wild and sweet as the clusters that grew in the valley of
  Eshcol.
Like a picture it seemed of the primitive, pastoral ages,
Fresh with the youth of the world, and recalling Rebecca
  and Isaac,
Old and yet ever new, and simple and beautiful always,
Love immortal and young in the endless succession of
  lovers.
So through the Plymouth woods passed onward the bridal
  procession.

A Golden Wedding

From "A GOLDEN WEDDING" [1]

By RUTH McENERY STUART

ON Sabbath morning following this Br'er Brown announced from the pulpit that at five o'clock on that same afternoon, immediately after the closing exercises of Conference, then in session, there would take place in the church a golden wedding, to which all were cordially invited. This was all. He refused further explanation, but laughingly bade the curious "come and see."

Needless to say, the church was crowded to overflowing, for curiosity ran high, both as to the individuals concerned and the exact nature of the promised ceremony. The expectant interest of the waiting congregation proved infectious, and after closing of Conference the dozen or more of ministers present remained, to a man, curious to witness an occasion so rare as a golden wedding.

After a short interval of some disorder, during which ministers and people engaged in social conversation, laughingly surmising as to who the bridal party should be, a stir at the door announced their approach.

Had not their dress labelled them as the heroes of the hour it would have been impossible, so great was the crowd, for them to have made their way up the aisle. The throng, pressing to right and left, gave way, however, and arm in arm the old couple, obeying orders, passed up the middle aisle and took their stand before the pulpit.

The groom wore his old broadcloth suit, — the very one, by the way, in which he had been married to this same woman a nameless number of years ago.

The bride, modestly attired in an old white muslin, might have escaped special notice in a crowd, except for a small

1 From "A Golden Wedding," published by Harper & Brothers.

spray of natural orange flowers which she wore upon her forehead.

It is a pity to write it, but there was a titter of mirth, ill suppressed, unworthy the dignity of the occasion or the place, as the old pair tottered up the aisle.

Brother Brown had stepped down before the pulpit and was ready to receive them. Perceiving instinctively that his congregation was not in touch with the spirit of the occasion, he won their attention and deference by a short and earnest prayer; then lowering his voice, addressed them solemnly as follows : —

"My deah bredren and sistern in de Lord, you see befo' you a aged couple, bofe o' whom an' each one o' which is no stranger ter you all — Br'er Alexander Thormson, a man in good an' reg'lar standin' in de chu'ch, an' Sister Cicely Garrett, lakwisely respected an' respectable 'mongst de sisterhood fur stiddy-goin' piety. It is a fac' well known ter dis corngergatiom dat dese two pussons is been livin' nex' do' ter one-'n'er fur de space o' six mont's er sech a matter, save an' exceptin' sech times as Sister Garrett is been livin' out at service; an' when I 'form you o' de fac' dat dee claims dat dee was married ter one-'n'er long 'fo' de wah, an' ain't reconnise one-'n'er tell now, 't ain't fur you ter 'spute dey words, 'caze when you cas'es yo' eyes upon 'em now, as dee stan' heah to-day; you can easy conceive o' de fac' dat de lan'marks *by* which dee *could* o' been reconnised is well-nigh washed away by de surgin' o' de river o' time. Dee claims dat dee was jined in de holy instate o' matrermony in de ole days, time dee was yong, an' arter meanderin' roun' de worl', eas' an' wes', norf an' souf, norfeas' an' norfwes', so ter speak ter all p'ints o' de cumpositiom, dee suddenly reconnise one-'n'er, an' now, while dee ain't a-ca'culatin' ter ketch up wid all de yeahs what 's gone, dee 'low dat dee crave ter come back ter de startin'-p'int an' start fresh, han' in han'. By de blessin' o' Gord, when dee 'skivered one-'n'er, dee was bofe free-handed an' free-hearted; an' now wid a free han' dee craves ter jine han's ag'in, an' wid a free heart dee craves ter jine hearts once mo'; an' ef dey hearts is bofe turned dat-a-way, who gwine say de word ter hender 'em? Ef anybordy got a word ag'in it, let 'im speak now er else, as de Bible say, fo' ever hol' 'is peace."

He hesitated, casting his eye over the crowd, upon which the silence of attentive listening had fallen.

" Hit 's true," he resumed, " dis aged couple is well on in yeahs, an' look lak dey journey is mos' done; but ef dee got de cour'ge ter teck han's fur de las' mile o' de road, 't ain't fur de lacks o' us ter *dis*cour'ge 'em! An' when I looks at dis o-ole man, ripe in yeahs, as de book say, an' 'cripit an' failin' in steps, an' I know dey 's a woman what 's willin' ter stan' up an' teck de 'spornserbility o' follerin' dat man clean tell 'e gits ter de gate o' de kingdom, I bless de Lord an' say, *dat woman got cour'ge, sho!* She is *born inter de light,* 'caze hit would be a dark journey *fur de onconverted!* An' when my eyes pass ter de bride — 't ain't no use fur me ter specify — but when my eyes pass ter de bride what stan's befo' me now, a-leanin' fon'ly on de arm o' de groom — dat same groom what done picked an' choosed 'er out, away back yonder time o' de fallin' o' de stars — 't ain't no use fur me ter specify, but I raises my eyes ter Heaven an' I say, Bless Gord fur cour'ge! De bride ain't show no more cour'ge 'n de groom is. Bless Gord fur a brave heart, an' a kin' heart, an' a true heart!

" *Wharfore,*" he continued, " in de face o' de fac's an' in de presence o' you all, I pernounce 'em once mo' *man and wife!* "

Turning to the groom, he added, lowering his voice, " I ain't say s'lute yo' bride, 'caze I know she done been s'luted on de former 'casiom; howsomever, ef you desires ter 'new yo' salutatiom 'fo' de worl', you is free ter do so."

The old man bent his head and kissed the lips of his old wife. This was taken as the usual signal for congratulations, and the congregation began to move forward. With a wave of his arm, however, the minister indicated that the golden wedding was not yet over. Placing bride and groom in chairs within the chancel, he turned again to the congregation. A change of tone announced that he was now approaching a new branch of the subject.

"I guv out dis mawnin'," he began, "dat dis was gwine ter be a *golden weddin'*, an' what is I mean, my breddern? Is I mean dat de *preacher* was rich? No, you know I ain't. Is I mean dat de *groom* was rich? No, you know he ain't. Is I mean dat de *bride* was rich? No, you know she ain't. Den what *is* I mean? What is de significatiom of a golden weddin'? Hit's de cilebratiom o' de ma'yage o' two pussons what have de cour'ge to stan' up 'fore Gord an' de worl' arter fifty yeahs, an' say 'Amen! Dee lived through it an' dee gwine stan' up ter it!' An' ef dee sorry dee done it dee nuver lets on. Dat's de weddin' part; an' de gol' part dat mean dat ev'ybordy bleege ter fetch a gol' weddin' present. Now fur de gol' part. In co'se I knows you ain't able ter come up wid pure gol', but look ter me lak dis is a proud occasiom ter do double juty wid sech as you is got, an' yo' knows yo'se'f dat small change is de squivalent o' gol'; an' now I tell you what I perpose ter do: I 'ain't c'lected no sal'ry fur two mont's, an' ef you'll all come up hearty, young an' ole wid de widder's mite, an' swell de collectiom, I tell you what I gwine do: I gwine 'vide up even wid de bride an' groom, an' we'll give az 'em a golden weddin' ter de best o' our stability, 'caze when a pair o' ole pussons show de cour'ge what dee done show ter-day, hit's on'y right ter he'p 'em 'long an' give 'em a start. What you say?"

"Amen!" exclaimed an old man in the front pew.

"Turn up de hat!" The voice came from the body of the church this time.

"Ole age boun' ter ketch us all ef we live," said another, — a white-haired sister.

It was pretty, the generous spirit of this most ingenuous and sympathetic people.

The collection was the largest ever known.

THE GOLDEN WEDDING.

Erdmann.

The Golden Wedding

From "THE GOLDEN WEDDING"[1]

By WILL CARLETON

TEN mile wood an' bramble, and three mile field an'
    dew,
In the cold smile of morning, I walked, to marry you;
No horse had I but my wishes — no pilot but a star;
But my boyish heart it fancied it heard you from afar.

So through the woods I hurried, an' through the grass an'
    dew,
An' little I thought o' tiring, the whole of my journey
    through;
Things ne'er before nor after do so a man rejoice,
As on the day he marries the woman of his choice!

And then our country wedding — brimful o' grief an' glee,
With every one a-pettin' an' jokin' you an' me;
The good cheer went and came, wife, as it sometimes has
    done
When clouds have chased each other across the summer
    sun.

There was your good old father dressed up in weddin'
    shape,
With all the homespun finery that he could rake an'
    scrape;
And your dear-hearted mother, the sunlight of whose smile
Shone through the showers of tear-drops that stormed her
    face the while;

Also your sisters an' brothers who hardly seemed to know
How they could scare up courage to let their sister go;

1 *From " Farm Festivals," published by Harper & Brothers.*

An' cousins an' school-house comrades, dressed up in
    meetin' trim,
With one of them a-sulkin' because it was n't him;

An' there was the good old parson, his neck all dressed in
    white,
A bunch o' texts in his left eye, a hymn-book in his right;
And the parson's virgin daughter, plain an' severely pure,
Who hoped we should be happy, but was n't exactly sure;

And there was the victuals, seasoned with kind regards an'
    love,
And holly-wreaths with breastpins of rubies, up above;
An' there was my heart a-wonderin' as how such things
    could be,
And there was all the world before us, and there was you
    and me.

FROM "THE BRIDE OF LAMMER-MOOR"

BY SIR WALTER SCOTT

THE morning dawned bright and cheerily. The bridal guests assembled in gallant troops from distant quarters. Not only the relations of Sir William Ashton, and the still more dignified connections of his lady, together with the numerous kinsmen and allies of the bridegroom, were present upon this joyful ceremony, gallantly mounted, arrayed, and caparisoned, but almost every Presbyterian family of distinction, within fifty miles, made a point of attendance upon an occasion which was considered as giving a sort of triumph over the Marquis of A——, in the person of his kinsman. Splendid refreshments awaited the guests on their arrival, and after these were finished, the cry was to horse. The bride was led forth betwixt her brother Henry and her mother. Her gaiety of the preceding day had given way to a deep shade of melancholy, which, however, did not misbecome an occasion so momentous. There was a light in her eyes, and a colour in her cheek, which had not been kindled for many a day, and which, joined to her great beauty, and the splendour of her dress, occasioned her entrance to be greeted with an universal murmur of applause, in which even the ladies could not refrain from joining. While the cavalcade were getting to horse, Sir William Ashton, a man of peace and of form, censured his son Henry for having begirt himself with a military sword of preposterous length, belonging to his brother, Colonel Ashton.

"If you must have a weapon," he said, " upon such a peaceful occasion, why did you not use the short poniard sent from Edinburgh on purpose?"

The boy vindicated himself, by saying it was lost.

"You put it out of the way yourself, I suppose," said his father, "out of ambition to wear that preposterous thing, which might have served Sir William Wallace. But never mind, get to horse now, and take care of your sister."

The boy did so, and was placed in the centre of the gallant train. At the time he was too full of his own appearance, his sword, his laced cloak, his feathered hat, and his managed horse, to pay much regard to anything else; but he afterward remembered to the hour of his death, that when the hand of his sister, by which she supported herself on the pillion behind him, touched his own, it felt as wet and cold as sepulchral marble.

Glancing wide over hill and dale, the fair bridal procession at last reached the parish church, which they nearly filled; for, besides domestics, above a hundred gentlemen and ladies were present upon the occasion. The marriage ceremony was performed according to the rites of the Presbyterian persuasion, to which Bucklaw of late had judged it proper to conform.

On the outside of the church a liberal dole was distributed to the poor of the neighbouring parishes, under the direction of Johnny Mortheuch, who had lately been promoted from his desolate quarters at the Hermitage, to fill the more eligible situation of sexton at the parish church of Ravenswood. Dame Gourlay, with two of her contemporaries, the same who assisted at Alice's late wake, seated apart upon a flat monument, or *through-stane*, sate enviously comparing the shares which had been allotted to them in dividing the dole.

"Johnny Mortheuch," said Annie Winnie, "might hae minded auld lang syne, and thought of his auld kimmers, for as braw as he is with his new black coat. I hae gotten but five herring instead o' sax, and this disna look like a gude saxpennys, and I dare say this bit morsel o' beef is an unce lighter than ony that's been dealt round; and it's a bit o' the tenony hough, mair by token, that yours, Maggie, is out o' the back sey."

THE WEDDING RING.

Willems.

"Mine, quo' she?" mumbled the paralytic hag, "mine is half banes, I trow. If grit folk gie poor bodies onything for coming to their weddings and burials, it suld be something that wad do them gude, I think."

"Their gifts," said Ailsie Gourlay, "are dealt for nae love of us — nor out of respect for whether we feed or starve. They wad gie us whinstanes for loaves, if it would serve their ain vanity, and yet they expect us to be as grateful as they ca' it, as if they served us for true love and liking."

"And that's truly said," answered her companion.

"But, Ailsie Gourlay, ye're the auldest o' us three, did ye ever see a mair grand bridal?"

"I winna say that I have," answered the hag; "but I think soon to see as braw a burial."

"And that wad please me as weel," said Annie Winnie; "for there's as large a dole, and folk are no obliged to girn and laugh, and mak murgeons, and wish joy to these hellicat quality, that lord it ower us like brute beasts. I like to pack the dead-dole in my lap, and rin ower my auld rhyme.

> "'My loaf in my lap, my penny in my purse,
> Thou art ne'er the better, and I'm ne'er the worse.'"

"That's right, Annie," said the paralytic woman; "God send us a green Yule and a fat kirkyard!"

"But I wad like to ken, Luckie Gourlay, for ye're the auldest and wisest amang us, whilk o' these revellers' turns it will be to be streekit first?"

"D'ye see yon dandilly maiden," said Dame Gourlay, "a' glistenin' wi' goud and jewels, that they are lifting upon the white horse behind that hare-brained callant in scarlet, wi' the lang sword at his side?"

"But that's the bride!" said her companion, her cold heart touched with some sort of compassion; "that's the very bride hersell! Eh, whow! sae young, sae braw, and sae bonny — and is her time sae short?"

"I tell ye," said the sibyl, "her winding-sheet is up as

high as her throat already, believe it wha list. Her sand has but few grains to rin out, and nae wonder — they 've been weel shaken. The leaves are withering fast on the trees, but she 'll never see the Martinmas wind gar them dance in swirls like the fairy rings."

" Ye waited on her for a quarter," said the paralytic woman, " and got twa red pieces, or I am far beguiled."

" Ay, ay," answered Ailsie, with a bitter grin; " and Sir William Ashton promised me a bonny red gown to the boot o' that — a stake, and a chain, and a tar barrel, lass ! — what think ye o' that for a propine ? — for being up early and doun late for fourscore nights and mair wi' his dwining daughter. But he may keep it for his ain leddy, cummers."

" I hae heard a sough," said Annie Winnie, " as if Leddy Ashton was nae canny body."

" D' ye see her yonder," said Dame Gourlay, " as she prances on her gray gelding out at the kirkyard ? — there 's mair o' utter deevilry in that woman, as brave and fair-fashioned as she rides yonder, than in a' the Scotch witches that ever flew by moonlight ower North-Berwick Law."

" What 's that ye say about witches, ye d——d hags ? " said Johnny Mortheuch ; " are ye casting yer cantrips in the very kirkyard, to mischieve the bride and bridegroom ? Get awa hame, for if I tak my souple t' ye, I 'll gar ye find the road faster than ye wad like."

" Hech, sirs ! " answered Ailsie Gourlay ; " how bra' are we wi' our new black coat and our weel-pouthered head as if we had never kend hunger nor thirst oursells ! and we 'll be screwing up our bit fiddle, doubtless, in the ha' the night, amang a' the other elbo'-jiggers for miles round. Let 's see if the pins haud, Johnny — that 's a', lad."

" I take ye a' to witness, gude people," said Mortheuch, " that she threatens me wi' mischief, and forspeaks me. If onything but gude happens to me or my fiddle this night, I 'll make it the blackest night's job she ever stirred in. I 'll hae her before Presbytery and Synod — I 'm half a minister mysell, now that I'm a bedral in an inhabited parish."

Although the mutual hatred betwixt these hags and the rest of mankind had steeled their hearts against all impressions of festivity, this was by no means the case with the multitude at large. The splendour of the bridal retinue, the gay dresses, the spirited horses, the blithesome appearance of the handsome women and gallant gentlemen assembled upon the occasion, had the usual effect upon the minds of the populace. The repeated shouts of " Ashton and Bucklaw for ever ! " — the discharge of pistols, guns, and musketoons, to give what was called the bridal-shot, evinced the interest the people took in the occasion of the cavalcade, as they accompanied it upon their return to the castle. If there was here and there an elder peasant or his wife who sneered at the pomp of the upstart family, and remembered the days of the long-descended Ravenswoods, even they, attracted by the plentiful cheer which the castle that day afforded to rich and poor, held their way thither, and acknowledged, notwithstanding their prejudices, the influence of *l'Amphitrion où l'on dine*.

Thus accompanied with the attendance both of rich and poor, Lucy returned to her father's house. Bucklaw used his privilege of riding next to the bride, but, new to such a situation, rather endeavoured to attract attention by the display of his person and horsemanship, than by any attempt to address her in private. They reached the castle in safety, amid a thousand joyous acclamations.

It is well known that the weddings of ancient days were celebrated with a festive publicity rejected by the delicacy of modern times. The marriage guests, on the present occasion, were regaled with a banquet of unbounded profusion, the relics of which, after the domestics had feasted in their turn, were distributed among the shouting crowd, with as many barrels of ale as made the hilarity without correspond to that within the castle. The gentlemen, according to the fashion of the times, indulged, for the most part, in deep draughts of the richest wines, while the

53

ladies, prepared for the ball which always closed a bridal entertainment, impatiently expected their arrival in the state gallery. At length the social party broke up at a late hour, and the gentlemen crowded into the saloon, where, enlivened by wine and the joyful occasion, they laid aside their swords, and handed their impatient partners to the floor. The music already rang from the gallery, along the fretted roof of the ancient state apartment. According to strict etiquette, the bride ought to have opened the ball, but Lady Ashton, making an apology on account of her daughter's health, offered her own hand to Bucklaw as substitute for her daughter's.

FROM "THE BANKS OF THE LEE"

BY THOMAS DAVIS

O, THE banks of the Lee, the banks of the Lee,
    And love in a cottage for Mary and me!
There's not in the land a lovelier tide,
And I'm sure that there's no one so fair as my bride.
    She's modest and meek,
    There's a down on her cheek,
    And her skin is as sleek
      As a butterfly's wing;
    Then her step would scarce show
    On the fresh-fallen snow,
    And her whisper is low,
      But as clear as the spring.
O, the banks of the Lee, the banks of the Lee,
And love in a cottage for Mary and me!
I know not how love is happy elsewhere,
I know not how any but lovers are there.

From "THE DEAD SECRET"[1]

By WILKIE COLLINS

THE church of Long Beckley (a large agricultural village in one of the midland counties of England), although a building in no way remarkable either for its size, its architecture, or its antiquity, possesses, nevertheless, one advantage which mercantile London has barbarously denied to the noble cathedral church of St. Paul. It has plenty of room to stand in, and it can consequently be seen with perfect convenience from every point of view all round the compass.

The large open space around the church can be approached in three different directions. There is a road from the village, leading straight to the principal door. There is a broad gravel walk, which begins at the vicarage gates, crosses the churchyard, and stops, as in duty bound, at the vestry entrance. There is a footpath over the fields, by which the lord of the manor, and the gentry in general who live in his august neighbourhood, can reach the side door of the building, whenever their natural humility may incline them to encourage Sabbath observance in the stables by going to church, like the lower sort of worshippers, on their own legs.

At half-past seven o'clock, on a certain fine summer morning, in the year eighteen hundred and forty-four, if any observant stranger had happened to be standing in some unnoticed corner of the churchyard, and to be looking about him with sharp eyes, he would probably have been the witness of proceedings which might have led him to believe that there was a conspiracy going on in Long Beckley, of which the church was the rallying point, and some of the most respectable inhabitants the principal

1 *From " The Dead Secret," published by Harper & Brothers.*

leaders. Supposing him to have been looking toward the vicarage as the clock chimed the half-hour, he would have seen the vicar of Long Beckley, the Reverend Doctor Chennery, leaving his house suspiciously, by the back way, glancing behind him guiltily as he approached the gravel walk that led to the vestry, stopping mysteriously just out-side the door, and gazing anxiously down the road that led to the village.

Assuming that our observant stranger would, upon this, keep out of sight, and look down the road, like the vicar, he would next have seen the clerk of the church — an aus-tere, yellow-faced man, — a Protestant Loyola in appear-ance, and a working shoemaker by trade — approaching with a look of unutterable mystery on his face, and a bunch of big keys in his hands. He would have seen the vicar nod in an abstracted manner to the clerk, and say, " Fine morning, Thomas. Have you had your breakfast yet ? " He would have heard Thomas reply, with a suspicious re-gard for minute particulars, " I have had a cup of tea and a crust, sir." And he would then have seen these two local conspirators, after looking up with one accord at the church clock, draw off together to the side door which com-manded a view of the footpath across the fields.

Following them, as our inquisitive stranger could not fail to do, he would have detected three more conspirators ad-vancing along the footpath. The leader of this treasonable party was an elderly gentleman, with a weather-beaten face, and a bluff, hearty manner. His two followers were a young gentleman and a young lady, walking arm-in-arm and talking together in whispers. They were dressed in the plainest morning costume. The faces of both were rather pale, and the manner of the lady was a little flurried. Otherwise there was nothing remarkable to observe in them, until they came to the wicket-gate leading into the church-yard ; and there the conduct of the young man seemed, at first sight, rather inexplicable. Instead of holding the gate open for the lady to pass through, he hung back, allowed her to open it for herself, waited till she had got to the churchyard side, and then, stretching out his hand over the gate, allowed her to lead him through the entrance, as if he had suddenly changed from a grown man to a helpless little child.

Noting this, and remarking also that, when the party from the fields had arrived within greeting distance of the vicar, and when the clerk had used his bunch of keys to open the church-door, the young lady's companion was led into the building (this time by Doctor Chennery's hand), as he had previously been led through the wicket gate, our observant stranger must have arrived at one inevitable conclusion, — that the person requiring such assistance as this was suffering under the affliction of blindness. Startled a little by that discovery, he would have been still further amazed, if he had looked into the church, by seeing the blind man and the young lady stand together before the altar rails, with the elderly gentleman in parental attendance. Any suspicions he might now entertain that the bond which united the conspirators at that early hour of the morning was of the hymeneal sort, and that the object of their plot was to celebrate a wedding with the strictest secrecy, would have been confirmed in five minutes by the appearance of Doctor Chennery from the vestry in full canonicals, and by the reading of the marriage service in the reverend gentleman's most harmonious officiating tones. The ceremony concluded, the attendant stranger must have been more perplexed than ever by observing that the persons concerned in it all separated, the moment the signing, the kissing and congratulating duties proper to the occasion had been performed, and quickly retired in the various directions by which they had approached the church.

Leaving the clerk to return by the village road, the bride, bridegroom, and elderly gentleman to turn back by the footpath over the fields, and the visionary stranger of these pages to vanish out of them in any direction that he pleases, let us follow Doctor Chennery to the vicarage breakfast-table, and hear what he has to say about his professional exertions of the morning in the familiar atmosphere of his own family circle.

The Dead Secret

The persons assembled at the breakfast were, first, Mr.
Phippen, a guest; secondly, Miss Sturch, a governess;
thirdly, fourthly, and fifthly, Miss Louisa Chennery (aged
eleven years), Miss Amelia Chennery (aged nine years), and
Master Robert Chennery (aged eight years). There was
no mother's face present to make the household picture
complete. Doctor Chennery had been a widower since
the birth of his youngest child.

. . . .

As soon as the vicar entered the breakfast-parlor, the
children assailed him with a chorus of shouts. He was a
severe disciplinarian in the observance of punctuality at
meal-times; and he now stood convicted by the clock of
being too late for breakfast by a quarter of an hour.

"Sorry to have kept you waiting, Miss Sturch," said the
vicar, "but I have a good excuse for being late this
morning."

"Pray don't mention it, sir," said Miss Sturch, blandly
rubbing her plump little hands one over the other. "A
beautiful morning. I fear we shall have another warm
day. — Robert, my love, your elbow is on the table. —
A beautiful morning, indeed!"

"Stomach still out of order, eh, Phippen?" asked the
vicar, beginning to carve the ham.

Mr. Phippen shook his large head dolefully, placed his
yellow forefinger, ornamented with a large turquoise ring,
on the centre check of his light summer waistcoat, looked
piteously at Doctor Chennery and sighed, removed the finger, and produced from the breast pocket of his wrapper a
little mahogany case, took out of it a neat pair of apothecary's scales, with the accompanying weights, a morsel of
ginger and a highly polished silver nutmeg-grater. "Dear
Miss Sturch will pardon an invalid?" said Mr. Phippen,
beginning to grate the ginger feebly into the nearest teacup.

"Guess what has made me a quarter of an hour late this
morning," said the vicar, looking mysteriously all around
the table.

59

" Lying in bed, papa," cried the three children, clapping their hands in triumph.

"What do *you* say, Miss Sturch?" asked Doctor Chennery.

Miss Sturch smiled as usual, rubbed her hands as usual, cleared her throat softly as usual, looked at the tea-urn, and begged, with the most graceful politeness, to be excused if she said nothing.

"Your turn now, Phippen," said the vicar. " Come, guess what has kept me late this morning."

" My dear friend," said Mr. Phippen, giving the doctor a brotherly squeeze of the hand, " don't ask me to guess; I know! I saw what you eat at dinner yesterday. I saw what you drank after dinner. No digestion could stand it, not even yours. Guess what has made you late this morning? Pooh! pooh! I know. You dear, good soul, you have been taking physic! "

" Have n't touched a drop, thank God, for the last ten years! " said Doctor Chennery, with a look of devout gratitude. " No, no; you are all wrong. The fact is, I have been to church; and what do you think I have been doing there? Listen, Miss Sturch, listen, girls, with all your ears. Poor blind young Frankland is a happy man at last. I have married him to our dear Rosamond Treverton this very morning! "

" Without telling us, papa! " cried the two girls together, in their shrillest tones of vexation and surprise. " Without telling us, when you knew how we should have liked to see it ! "

" That was the very reason why I did not tell you, my dears," answered the vicar. " Young Frankland has not got so used to his affliction yet, poor fellow, as to bear being publicly pitied and stared at in the character of a blind bridegroom. He had such a nervous horror of being an object of curiosity on his wedding day, and Rosamond, like a kind-hearted girl as she is, was so anxious that his slightest caprices should be humoured, that we settled to have the wedding at an hour in the morning when no idlers were likely to be lounging about the neighbourhood of the

A Chinese Wedding.

church. I was bound over to the strictest secrecy about the day, and so was my clerk Thomas. Excepting us two, and the bride and bridegroom, and the bride's father, Captain Treverton, nobody knew — "

" Treverton ! " exclaimed Mr. Phippen, holding his tea-cup, with the grated ginger in the bottom of it, to be filled by Miss Sturch, " Treverton ! (No more tea, dear Miss Sturch.) How very remarkable ! I know the name. (Fill up with water, if you please.) Tell me, my dear doctor (many, many thanks ; no sugar — it turns to acid on the stomach), is this Miss Treverton whom you have been marrying many thanks again ; no milk, either) one of the Cornish Trevertons ? "

" To be sure she is ! " rejoined the vicar. " Her father, Captain Treverton, is the head of the family. Not that there 's much family to speak of now. The Captain, and Rosamond, and that whimsical old brute of an uncle of hers, Andrew Treverton, are the last left now of the old stock — a rich family and a fine family in former times — good friends to church and state, you know, and all that — "

. . . " Chennery, you dear good soul, what were we talking about ? Ah ! the bride — the interesting bride ! And so she is one of the Cornish Trevertons ? I knew something of Andrew years ago. He was a bachelor, like myself, Miss Sturch. His apparatus was out of order, like mine, dear Amelia. Not at all like his brother, the Captain, I should suppose ? And so she is married ? A charming girl, I have no doubt. A charming girl ! "

" No better, truer, prettier girl in the world," said the vicar.

" A very lively, energetic person," remarked Miss Sturch.

" How I shall miss her ! " cried Miss Louisa. " No-body else amused me as Rosamond did, when I was laid up with that last bad cold of mine."

" She used to give us such nice little early supper-parties," said Miss Amelia.

" She was the only girl I ever saw who was fit to play

with boys," said Master Robert. " She could catch a ball, Mr. Phippen, Sir, with one hand, and go down a slide with both her legs together."

" Bless me!" said Mr. Phipppen. " What an extraordinary wife for a blind man! You said he was blind from his birth, my dear doctor, did you not? Let me see, what was his name? You will not bear too hardly on my loss of memory, Miss Sturch? When indigestion has done with the body, it begins to prey on the mind. Mr. Frank Something, was it not?"

" No, no — Frankland," answered the vicar, " Leonard Frankland. And not blind from birth, by any means. It is not much more than a year ago since he could see almost as well as any of us."

. . . " You shock me; my dear Chennery, you shock me dreadfully," said Mr. Phippen. " Especially when you state that theory about long weakness after illness. Good Heavens! Why, *I* have had long weaknesses — I have got them now. Spots did he see before his eyes? I see spots, black spots, dancing black spots, dancing black bilious spots. Upon my word of honour, Chennery, this comes home to me — my sympathies are painfully acute — I feel this blind story in every nerve of my body; I do, indeed!"

" You would hardly know that Leonard was blind, to look at him," said Miss Louisa, striking into the conversation with a view to restoring Mr. Phippen's equanimity. " Except that his eyes look quieter than other people's, there seems no difference in them now. Who was that famous character you told us about, Miss Sturch, who was blind, and didn't show it any more than Leonard Frankland?"

" Milton, my love. I begged you to remember that he was the most famous of British epic poets," answered Miss Sturch, with suavity. " He poetically describes his blindness as being caused by ' so thick a drop serene.' You shall read about it, Louisa. After we have had a little French, we will have a little Milton, this morning. Hush, love, your papa is speaking."

"Poor young Frankland!" said the vicar, warmly. "That good, tender, noble creature I married him to this morning seems sent as a consolation to him in his affliction. If any human being can make him happy for the rest of his life, Rosamond Treverton is the girl to do it."

"She has made a sacrifice," said Mr. Phippen; "but I like her for that, having made a sacrifice myself in remaining single. It seems indispensable, indeed, that I should do so. How could I conscientiously inflict such a digestion as mine on a member of the fairer portion of creation? No; I am a sacrifice in my own proper person, and I have a fellow-feeling for others who are like me. Did she cry much, Chennery, when you were marrying her?"

"Cry!" exclaimed the vicar, contemptuously. "Rosamond Treverton is not one of the puling, sentimental sort, I can tell you. A fine, buxom, warm-hearted, quick-tempered girl, who looks what she means when she tells a man she is going to marry him. And, mind you, she has been tried. If she had n't loved him with all her heart and soul, she might have been free months ago to marry anybody she pleased. They were engaged long before this cruel affliction befell young Frankland, the fathers on both sides having lived as near neighbours in these parts for years. Well, when the blindness came, Leonard at once offered to release Rosamond from her engagement. You should have read the letter she wrote to him, Phippen, upon that. I don't mind confessing that I blubbered like a baby over it when they showed it to me. I should have married them at once the instant I read it, but old Frankland was a fidgety, punctilious kind of man, and he insisted on a six months' probation, so that she might be certain of knowing her own mind. He died before the term was out, and that caused the marriage to be put off again. But no delays could alter Rosamond, — six years, instead of six months, would not have changed her. There she was this morning as fond of that poor, patient blind fellow as she was the first day they were engaged. 'You shall never know a sad moment, Lenny, if I can help it, as long as you live,'

— these were the first words she said to him when we all came out of church. 'I hear you, Rosamond,' said I. 'And you shall judge me, too, Doctor,' says she, quick as lightning. 'We will come back to Long Beckley, and you shall ask Lenny if I have not kept my word.' With that she gave me a kiss that you might have heard down here at the vicarage, bless her heart! We'll drink her health after dinner, Miss Sturch — we'll drink both their healths, Phippen, in a bottle of the best wine I have in my cellar."

"In a glass of toast-and-water, so far as I am concerned, if you will allow me," said Mr. Phippen, mournfully.

The Bridal

From "THE BRIDAL"

By FREDERICK TENNYSON

THE bridal bells are pealing!
    We will rejoice to-day!
The blissful sounds are stealing
    Hearts away;

The jocund bells are pealing fast and sweet,
    Softly they come and go like lovers' sighs;
In one glad thought the young and old are met,
    The simple and the wise.

They reach the woodman in the morning air,
They reach the baron in his carven chair,
The dark-eyed damsel bending o'er the spring,
The scholar in dim cloister murmuring;
The dusty pilgrim stays across the stile;
The smith upon his anvil leans awhile;
Boys whistle — beggars bustle — shepherds sing —
The marriage bells ring merrily; hark, they ring.

The sun is kissing off from wood-nymphs' eyes
Their evening tears, and dewy breathings rise
From wildflower urns — o'er waving fields of wheat
Swift shadows stream away, and woodnotes fleet
From frolic finches tremble here and there
'Mid the loud carols and the breezy air —
I hear blithe tongues and tread of rustic feet,
The joyous bells are pealing fast and sweet.

Of life, and love, and luck the countryfolk
Discourse by riverside, and hedgerow oak,

5   65

Of fairy gifts, and wondrous fortune after,
They tell with faith, with antique songs and laughter;
If one rude tongue should jar and seek to shame
The bride's new honours with her humble name,
" Thou in her place wouldst merit thine own jest,"
They cry — but she is better than their best.

> The happy bells are chiming;
>   Here comes the peerless bride,
> A mighty host is climbing
>   The hillside;

> Through briery by-path and o'er sunny down
>   They haste unto the bridal, for to-day
> The lord of half the country and the town
>   Shall lead his bride away.

Who is the bride ?   A simple village maid —
Beauty and Truth — a violet in the shade,
But she shall show proud Sin and painted Scorn
That Truth and Beauty are to honour born;
He teach proud hearts to feel, proud eyes to see
How strong is Nature, winged Love how free :
Long be their days, their fortunes glad and sure —
His blood is noble and her heart is pure.

Look on her — in that aspect ye may spy
Her mirrored soul where all sweet pictures lie;
Spring, summer, with their changes o'er it flit,
And morn and eve, twin sisters, look from it;
While memories of green woods and tuneful streams,
Lone songs and autumn sighs, and April gleams
In shadows of soft melancholy flow
Up from her heart across her crownèd brow.

.   .   .   .

Oh! what rare thoughts are his, oh! what delight
To gaze upon her, hold her in his sight,

The Bridal

To quaff her smiles as thirsty bees that sup,
Nuzzled within a noonday lily's cup,
The last sweets, lest a drop be there in vain ;
And in that rapture all remembered pain
Exhales, and for a moment he can see
A lightning flash of what the Soul shall be !

Wedding Day in Literature and Art

From "GUNNAR, A TALE OF NORSE LIFE" [1]

By HJALMAR HJÖRTH BOYESEN

GUNNAR knew the Berg daughters; for wherever there was dancing and merry-making they were as sure to be as the fiddlers. As far back as he could remember, the church road had never missed the " Wild Ducks " from Berg, as they were generally called, because they all were dressed alike, were all fair and gay, and where one went the rest would invariably follow. Now one of the Wild Ducks was to be married to a rich old bachelor from the neighbouring valley, and people knew that Peer Berg intended to make a wedding the fame of which should echo through seven parishes round. Summons for the wedding were sent out far and wide, and to Gunnar with the rest.

It was early in the morning when bride and bridegroom from Berg with their nearest kinsfolk cleared their boats, and set out for the church; on the way one boat of wedding guests joined them, and by the time they reached the landing-place in the " Parsonage Bay " their party counted quite a goodly number. The air was fresh and singularly transparent, and the fjord, partaking of the all-pervading air-tone, glittered in changing tints of pale blue and a cool, delicate green. Now and then a faint tremor would skim along its mirror, like the quiver of a slight but delightful emotion. Towards the North the mountains rose abruptly from the water, and with their snow-hooded heads loomed up into fantastic heights; irregular drifts of light, fog-like cloud hung or hovered about the lower crags. Westward the fjord described a wide curve, bounded by a lower plateau, which gradually ascended through the usual

Nuptial Festivity.

Bepschlag.

pine and birch regions into the eternal snow fields of im-
measurable dimensions; and through the nearest peaks the
view was opened into a mountain panorama of indescribable grandeur. There gigantic yokuls measured their
strength with the heavens; wild glaciers shot their arms
downwards, clutching the landscape in their cold embrace,
and rapid snow-fed rivers darted down between the preci-
pices where only a misty spray, hovering over the chasm,
traced their way toward the rjord.

About half-way between the church and the mouth of
the river a headland, overgrown with birch and pine forest,
ran far out into the fjord. Here the first four boats of
the bridal party stopped on their homeward way to wait
for those which had been left behind; in one sat the bride
herself, with breast-plate and silver crown on her head, and
at her side the bridegroom shining in his best holiday
trim, with rows of silver buttons and buckles, according
to the custom of the valley; in his hand he held an ancient
war-axe. On the bench in front of them Peer Berg and
his merry wife had their places; and next to them, again,
two of the bridegroom's nearest kin. The second boat
contained the remaining Wild Ducks and other relatives
and connections; and the third and fourth wedding guests
and musicians. But there were at least nine or ten loads
missing yet; for the wedding at Berg was to be no ordinary one. In the mean time old Peer proposed to taste
the wedding brewage, and bade the musicians to strike up
so merry a tune that it should sing through the bone and
the marrow. "For fiddles, like hops, give strength to
beer," said he, "and then people from afar will hear that
the bridal boats are coming." And swinging above his
head a jug filled to the brim with strong home-brewed
Hardanger-beer, he pledged the company and quaffed the
liquor to the last drop. "So did our old forefathers drink,"
cried he; "the horn might stand on either end if their lips
had once touched it. And may it be said from this day,
that the wedding guests at Berg proved that they had the
true old Norse blood in their veins."

A turbulent applause followed this speech of Peer's, and amid music, singing, and laughter the beer-jugs passed from boat to boat and from hand to hand. Now and then a loud yodling halloo came floating through the calm air, followed by a clear, manifold echo; and no sooner had the stillness closed over it than the merry voices from the boats again rose in louder and noisier chorus. All this time the bridal fleet was rapidly increasing, and for every fresh arrival the beer-jugs made another complete round. No one drank without finding something to admire, whether it were the liquor itself or the skilfully carved silver jugs in which, as every one knew, Peer Berg took no little pride; indeed, they had been heirlooms in the family from immemorial times, and the saying was that even kings had drunk from them.

There were now eighteen or nineteen boats assembled about the point of the headland, and the twentieth and last was just drawing up its oars for a share of the beer and the merriment. In the stern sat Gunnar, dreamily gazing down into the deep, and at his side his old friend Rhyme-Ola, his winking eyes fixed on him with an anxious expression of almost motherly care and tenderness. In his hands he held some old, time-worn paper, to which he quickly directed his attention whenever Gunnar made the slightest motion, as if he were afraid of being detected. When the customary greetings were exchanged, the bride-groom asked Rhyme-Ola to let the company hear his voice, and the singer, as usual, readily complied. It was the old, mournful tale of Young Kirsten and the Merman; and as he lent his rich, sympathetic voice to the simplicity of the ballad, its pathos became the more touching, and soon the tears glittered in many a tender-hearted maiden's eye.

There is a deep, unconscious romance in the daily life of the Norwegian peasant. One might look in vain for a scene like this throughout Europe, if for no other reason than because the *fjord* is a peculiarly Norwegian feature, being, in life, tone, and character, as different from the friths of Scotland and the bays of the Mediterranean as the hoary rugged pines of the North are from those slender, smooth-grown things which in the South bear the same name. Imagine those graceful strong-built boats, rocking over their own images reflected in the cool transparence of the fjord; the fresh, fair-haired maidens scattered in blooming clusters among the elderly, more sedately dressed matrons; and the old men, whose weather-worn faces and rugged expressive features told of natures of the genuine mountain mould. The young lads sat on the row-benches, some with the still dripping oars poised under their knees, while they silently listened to the song; others bending eagerly forward or leaning on their elbows, dividing their attention between Rhyme-Ola and the tittering girls on the benches in front. They all wore red pointed caps, generally with the tassels hanging down over one side of the forehead, which gave a certain touch of roguishness and light-heartedness to their manly and clear-cut visages. And to complete the picture there is Rhyme-Ola, as he sits aloft on the beer-kegs in the stern of the boat, now and then striking out with his ragged arms, and weeping and laughing as the varying incidents of his song affect him. As a background to this scene stands the light birch forest glittering with its fresh sprouts, and filling the air with its spring-like fragrance; behind this again the pines raise their dusky heads; and around the whole picture the mountains close their gigantic arms and warmly press forest, fjord, and bridal party to the mighty heart of Norway.

When the ballad was at an end, it was some time before any one spoke, for no one wished to be the first to break the silence.

"Always the same mournful tales," said at length one of the old men, but only half aloud as if he were speaking to himself.

"Rhyme-Ola," cried one of the fiddlers, "why don't you learn to sing something jolly, instead of the sad old things, which could almost make a stone weep?"

"You might just as well tell the plover to sing like the lark," answered Rhyme-Ola.

"I like the old songs," said Ragnhild Rimul (for she was there also); "they always bring tears to my eyes, but sometimes I like better to cry than to laugh."

Peer Berg now signalled to the oarsmen, and the boats soon shot swiftly in through the fjord. In about an hour the whole company landed on the Berg pier, and marched in procession up to the wedding house. First came the musicians, then the bride and bridegroom, and after them their parents and nearest kin. The guests formed the rear. Among the last were Lars Henjum and Ragnhild; last of all came Gunnar and Rhyme-Ola.

Berg was an old-fashioned place, for Peer Berg took a special pride in being old-fashioned. Coming up the hill from the water, Berg appeared more like a small village than a single family dwelling. The mansion itself in which Peer with his wife and his Wild Ducks resided, was of a most peculiar shape. It was very large and had two stories, the upper surrounded by a huge balcony, which made it appear nearly twice as broad as the lower. Over this balcony shot out a most venerable slated roof, completely overgrown with moss, grass, and even shrubs of considerable size; the railing, which had once been painted and skilfully carved, was so high and so close that it afforded little or no room for the daylight to peep in and cheer the dreary nest of the Wild Ducks. Round the mansion lay a dozen smaller houses and cottages, scattered in all directions; if they had grown out from the soil of their own accord, they could hardly have got into more awkward or more irregular positions. One looked north, another west, a third southeast, and no two lay parallel or with their gables facing each other. Every one of these houses, however, had been created for some special purpose. First, there were, of course, the barns and the stables, which in size and respectability nearly rivalled the mansion. Quite indispensable were the servant hall, the sheepfold, and the wash-house; and without forge and flax-house

Berg could hardly have kept up its reputation as a model establishment.

With gay music and noisy laughter and merriment, the bridal procession passed into the yard, where from the steps of the mansion they were greeted by the master of ceremonies in a high-flown speech of congratulation. The doors were then thrown wide open, and soon like a swelling tide the crowd rolled through the house, and the lofty halls shook with the hum and din of the festivity. For at such times the Norsemen are in their lustiest mood; then the old Saga-spirit is kindled again within them; and let him beware who durst say then that the Viking blood of the North is extinct. The festal hall at Berg, which occupied the whole lower floor of the building, was decorated for the occasion with fresh leaves and birch branches, for the birch is the bride of the trees; but as it was still early in the season, it was necessary to keep up a fire on the open hearth. This hearth, indeed, in more than one sense, may be said to have given a certain homely colour to everything present, not only in the remoter sense, as being the gathering place of the family in the long winter evenings, but also in a far nearer one; its smoke had, perhaps for more than a century, been equally shared by the chimney and the room, and had settled in the form of shining soot on walls, rafters, and ceiling.

Two long tables extended across the length of the hall from one wall to another, laden with the most tempting dishes. The seats of honour, of course, belonged to bride and bridegroom, and they having taken their places, the master of ceremonies urged the guests to the tables and arranged them in their proper order in accordance with their relative dignity or their relationship or acquaintance with the bride. Now the blessing was pronounced and the meal began. It was evident enough that the boating and the march had whetted the guests' appetites; huge trays of cream-porridge, masses of dried beef, and enormous wheaten loaves disappeared with astonishing rapidity. Toast upon toast was drunk, lively speeches made and heartily applauded, tales and legends told, and a tone of hearty, good-humoured merriment prevailed. The meal was a long one; when the feasters rose from the tables, it was already dusk.

In the course of the afternoon the weather had changed; now it was blowing hard, and the wind was driving huge masses of cloud in through the mountain gorges. Shadows sank over the valley, the torches were lit in the wedding house, and a lusty wood fire crackled and roared on the hearth. Then the tables were removed, the music began, and bride and bridegroom trod the springing dance together, according to ancient custom; others soon followed, and before long the floors and walls creaked and the flames of the torches rose and flickered in fitful motion, as the whirling air-currents seized and released them. Those of the men who did not dance joined the crowd round the beer-barrels, which stood in the corner opposite the hearth, and there slaked their thirst with the strong, home-brewed drink which Norsemen have always loved so well, and fell into friendly chat about the result of the late fishery or the probabilities for a favourable lumber and grain year.

From "THE BRIDAL MARCH"[1]

By BJÖRNSTJERNE BJÖRNSON

INGA, Mildred's cousin, who was now herself a wife, had come to attend to the adornment of the bride. This was done in the storehouse; the old chest, in which the bridal silver was kept, — the crown, the belt, the buckle, the brooches, the rings, — was brought forward. Grandmother had the key to it; she was there herself to open it, and Beret was with her, as her assistant. Mildred had already decked herself in her bridal dress, and all the finery that belonged to her, when this splendour (which Beret and the grandmother had polished the week before) was brought to light, glittering and heavy. Article after article was tried on. Beret held the glass for the bride. The old lady told how so many of her family had worn this silver on their wedding-day, and how the happiest of all had been her own mother, Aslaug Haugen.

Just then the old family bridal march was heard outside: every one in the storehouse paused, listened, then hastened to the door to see what was going on. The first person their eyes fell on was Endrid, the bride's father. He had seen Hans Haugen, and his brothers and sisters, come riding toward the gard; it was a rare thing for Endrid to have any unusual ideas; but this time it occurred to him that these guests should be received with the ancestral tune. He gave the fiddlers orders to go forward playing it; and there he now stood himself in their midst near the storehouse, holding in his hand a silver tankard filled with the wedding ale. Several others had joined him. Hans and his faithful brothers and sisters drove into the gard, and it was very evident that this reception touched them.

[1] *By special permission of Houghton, Mifflin & Co.*

An hour later, as a matter of course, the bridal march was struck up again; that was when the bride and bridegroom, and the bride's parents, and grandmother and Beret, and the bridegroom's brothers and sisters came out in couples with the fiddlers at their head, to get into the carts. There are moments in our lives when all signs are favourable, and at such a moment the bridal party drove forth from Tingvold one bright spring day. At church there was assembled so great a multitude that no one remembered ever having seen anything to equal it. Every one in the crowd knew the family history, and how it was interwoven with this bridal march which now rang out jubilantly through the glad sunshine, its tones encircling the bride and bridegroom and the happy bridal party.

And because all their thoughts centred in this one, the priest, too, chose a text for the wedding discourse that afforded an opportunity of dwelling on the idea that children are the crowning glory of our lives when they are a reflection of *our* honour, our development, our labour.

On the way out of church Hans paused in front of the church door; he said something; the bride, in her supreme happiness, did not hear what it was, but she divined its meaning. He wanted her to look at Ole Haugen's grave, which was richly decked with flowers. She did so, and they passed out of the churchyard in such a way that their garments touched the headboard of his grave. The parents followed.

"ESTHONIAN BRIDAL SONG"

BY JOHANN GOTTFRIED VON HERDER

DECK thyself, maiden,
  With the hood of thy mother;
Put on the ribands
Which thy mother once wore:
On thy head the band of duty,
On thy forehead the band of care.
Sit in the seat of thy mother,
And walk in thy mother's footsteps.
And weep not, weep not, maiden:
If thou weep in thy bridal attire,
Thou wilt weep all thy life.

Wedding Day in Literature and Art

From "BRACEBRIDGE HALL"

By Washington Irving

NOTWITHSTANDING the doubts and the demurs of Lady Lillycraft, and all the grave objections conjured up against the month of May, the wedding has at last happily taken place. It was celebrated at the village church, in presence of a numerous company of relatives and friends, and many of the tenantry. The Squire must needs have something of the old ceremonies observed on the occasion; so, at the gate of the churchyard, several little girls of the village, dressed in white, were in readiness with baskets of flowers, which they strewed before the bride; and the butler bore before her the bride-cup, a great silver embossed bowl, one of the family relics from the days of hard drinkers. This was filled with rich wine, and decorated with a bunch of rosemary, tied with gay ribbons, according to ancient custom.

"Happy is the bride the sun shines on," says the old proverb; and it was as sunny and auspicious a morning as heart could wish. The bride looked uncommonly beautiful; but, in fact, what woman does not look interesting on her wedding day? I know no sight more charming and touching than that of a young and timid bride, in her robes of virgin white, led up trembling to the altar. When I thus behold a lovely girl, in the tenderness of her years, forsaking the house of her fathers and the home of her childhood, and, with the implicit confiding and the sweet self-abandonment which belong to women, giving up all the world for the man of her choice; when I hear her, in the good old language of the ritual, yielding herself to him, "for better for worse, for richer for poorer, in sickness and in health, to love, honour and obey till death do us part," it brings to my mind the beautiful and affecting self-devotion of Ruth: "Whither thou goest I will go, and where

The Village Wedding.

Fildes.

thou lodgest I will lodge; thy people shall be my people and thy God my God."

The fair Julia was supported on the trying occasion by Lady Lillycraft, whose heart was overflowing with its wonted sympathy in all matters of love and matrimony. As the bride approached the altar, her face would be one moment covered with blushes and the next deadly pale; and she seemed almost ready to shrink from sight among her female companions.

I do not know what it is that makes every one serious, and, as it were, awe-struck, at a marriage ceremony; which is generally considered an occasion of festivity and rejoicing. As the ceremony was performing, I observed many a rosy face among the country girls turn pale, and I did not see a smile throughout the church. The young ladies from the Hall were almost as much frightened as if it had been their own case, and stole many a look of sympathy at their trembling companion. A tear stood in the eye of the sensitive Lady Lillycraft; and as to Phœbe Wilkins, who was present, she absolutely wept and sobbed aloud; but it is hard to tell, half the time, what these fond foolish creatures are crying about.

The captain, too, though naturally gay and unconcerned, was much agitated on the occasion; and in attempting to put the ring upon the bride's finger, dropped it on the floor; which Lady Lillycraft has since assured me is a very lucky omen. Even Master Simon had lost his usual vivacity, and assumed a most whimsically solemn face, which he is apt to do on all occasions of ceremony. He had much whispering with the parson and parish-clerk, for he is always a busy personage in the scene, and he echoed the clerk's amen with a solemnity and devotion that edified the whole assemblage.

The moment, however, that the ceremony was over, the transition was magical. The bride-cup was passed round, according to ancient usage, for the company to drink to a happy union; every one's feelings seemed to break forth from restraint. Master Simon had a world of bachelor pleasantries to utter, and as to the gallant general, he bowed and cooed about the dulcet Lady Lillycraft like a mighty cock-pigeon about his dame.

The villagers gathered in the churchyard to cheer the happy couple as they left the church, and the musical tailor had marshalled his band, and set up a hideous discord, as the blushing and smiling bride passed through a lane of honest peasantry to her carriage. The children shouted and threw up their hats; the bells rang a merry peal that set all the crows and rooks flying and cawing about the air, and threatened to bring down the battlements of the old tower; and there was a continual popping off of rusty firelocks from every party of the neighbourhood.

The prodigal son distinguished himself on the occasion, having hoisted a flag on the top of the schoolhouse, and kept the village in a hubbub from sunrise, with the sound of drum and fife and pandean pipe; in which species of music several of his scholars are making wonderful proficiency. In his great zeal, however, he had nearly done mischief; for on returning from church, the horses of the bride's carriage took fright from the discharge of a row of old gun-barrels, which he had mounted as a park of artillery in front of the schoolhouse to give the captain a military salute as he passed.

The day passed off with great rustic rejoicing. Tables were spread under the trees in the park, where all the peasantry of the neighbourhood were regaled with roast-beef and plum-pudding, and oceans of ale. Ready-Money Jack presided at one of the tables, and became so full of good cheer as to unbend from his usual gravity, to sing a song all out of tune, and give two or three shouts of laughter that almost electrified his neighbours like so many peals of thunder. The schoolmaster and the apothecary vied with each other in making speeches over their liquor; and there were occasional glees and musical performances by the village band, that must have frightened every faun and dryad from the park. Even old Christy, who had got on a new dress from top to toe, and shone in all the splendour of bright leather breeches, and an enormous wedding favour in his cap, forgot his usual crustiness, became inspired by wine and wassail, and absolutely danced a hornpipe on one of the tables, with all the grace and agility of a mannikin hung upon wires.

Equal gaiety reigned within doors, where a large party of friends were entertained. Every one laughed at his own pleasantry, without attending to that of his neighbours. Loads of bride-cake were distributed. The young ladies were all busy in passing morsels of it through the wedding ring to dream on, and I myself assisted a little boarding-school girl in putting up a quantity for her companions, which I have no doubt will set all the little heads in the school gadding for a week at least.

After dinner all the company, great and small, abandoned themselves to the dance : not the modern quadrille, with its graceful gravity, but the merry, social, old country-dance : the true dance, as the Squire says, for a wedding occasion, as it sets all the world jigging in couples, hand in hand, and makes every eye and every heart dance merrily to the music. According to frank old usage, the gentle-folks of the Hall mingled for a time in the dance of the peasantry, who had a great tent erected for a ball-room ; and I think I never saw Master Simon more in his element than when figuring about among his rustic admirers as master of the ceremonies ; and with a mingled air of protection and gallantry, leading out the quondam Queen of May, all blushing at the signal honour conferred upon her.

In the evening the whole village was illuminated, ex-cepting the house of the radical, who had not shown his face during the rejoicings. There was a display of fire-works at the schoolhouse, got up by the prodigal son, which had wellnigh set fire to the building. The Squire is so pleased with the extraordinary services of this last-mentioned worthy, that he talks of enrolling him in his list of valuable retainers, and promoting him to some important post on the estate ; peradventure to be falconer, if the hawks can ever be brought into proper training.

Wedding Day in Literature and Art

There is a well-known old proverb, which says " one wedding makes many," — or something to the same purpose; and I should not be surprised if it holds good in the present instance. I have seen several flirtations among the young people brought together on this occasion; and a great deal of strolling about in pairs, among retired walks and blossoming shrubberies of the old garden : and if groves were really given to whispering, as poets would fain make us believe, Heaven knows what love-tales the grave-looking old trees about this venerable country-seat might blab to the world.

The general, too, has waxed very zealous in his devotions within the past few days, as the time of her ladyship's departure approaches. I observed him casting many a tender look at her during the wedding dinner, while the courses were changing; though he was always liable to be interrupted in his adoration by the appearance of any new delicacy. The general, in fact, has arrived at that time of life when the heart and stomach maintain a kind of balance of power, and when a man is apt to be perplexed in his affections between a fine woman and a truffled turkey. Her ladyship was certainly rivalled through the whole of the first course by a dish of stewed carp; and there was one glance which was evidently intended to be a point-blank shot at her heart, and could scarcely have failed to effect a practicable breach, had it not unluckily been directed away to a tempting breast of lamb, in which it immediately produced a formidable incision.

Thus did the faithless general go on, coquetting during the whole dinner, and committing an infidelity with every new dish ; until, in the end, he was so overpowered by the attentions he had paid to fish, flesh, and fowl, to pastry, jelly, cream, and blanc mange, that he seemed to sink within himself; his eyes swam beneath their lids, and their fire was so much slackened that he could no longer discharge a single glance that would reach across the table. Upon the whole, I fear the general ate himself into as much disgrace, at this memorable dinner, as I have seen him sleep himself into on a former occasion.

I am told, moreover, that young Jack Tibbets was so touched by the wedding ceremony, at which he was present, and so captivated by the sensibility of poor Phœbe Wilkins, who certainly looked all the better for her tears, that he had a reconciliation with her that very day after dinner, in one of the groves of the park, and danced with her in the evening, to the complete confusion of all Dame Tibbets's domestic politics.

From "ALICE AND UNA"

By DENIS FLORENCE MACCARTHY

A LICE was a chieftain's daughter,
    And though many suitors sought her,
She so loved Glengariff's water
That she let her lovers pine.
    Her eye was beauty's palace,
    And her cheek an ivory chalice,
    Through which the blood of Alice
Gleamed soft as rosiet wine.
And her lips like lusmore blossoms which the fairies
    intertwine
And her heart a golden mine.

. . . .

    Need we say that Maurice loved her,
    And that no blush reproved her
    When her throbbing bosom moved her
To give the heart she gave ?
    That by dawn-light and by twilight,
    And, O blessed moon, by thy light, —
    When the twinkling stars on high light
The wanderer o'er the wave, —
His steps unconscious led him where Glengariff's waters
    lave
Each mossy bank and cave.

. . . .

    The sun his gold is flinging,
    The happy birds are singing,
    And bells are gaily ringing

Along Glengariff's sea;
     And crowds in many a galley
     To the happy marriage rally
     Of the maiden of the valley
And the youth of Ceim-an-eich;
Old eyes with joy are weeping, as all ask on bended
     knee,
A blessing, gentle Alice, upon thee.

From "A MARRIAGE AT SEA"[1]

By W. CLARK RUSSELL

"BUT is it the fact, captain," I exclaimed, visited by a new emotion of surprise and incredulity, "that a marriage celebrated at sea by the captain of a ship is legal?"

. . . "Tell ye what I'll do!" he exclaimed, jumping up. "Do you know Mr. Higginson?"

"A passenger, I presume?"

"Ay, one of the shrewdest lawyers in New Zealand. I'll send for him, and you shall hear what he says."

But on putting his head out to call for the steward, he saw Mr. Higginson sitting at the saloon table, reading. Some whispering followed, and they both arrived, the captain carefully shutting the door behind him. Mr. Higginson was a tall, middle-aged man, with a face that certainly looked intellectual enough to inspire one with some degree of confidence in anything he might deliver. He put on a pair of *pince-nez* glasses, bowed to me, and took a chair. The captain began awkwardly, abruptly, and in a rumbling voice,—

"Mr. Higginson, I'll tell you in half a dozen words how the case stands. No need for mystery. Mr. Barclay's out on an eloping tour. He don't mind my saying so, for we want nothing but the truth aboard the 'Carthusian.' He's run away with that sweet young lady we took off his yacht, and is anxious to get married, and Mrs. Barstow and Miss Moggadore don't at all relish the situation the young lady's put herself in, and they're for marrying her as quickly as the job can be done."

---

[1] *By permission of J. B. Lippincott Co., from "A Marriage at Sea" by W. Clark Russell.*

GOING TO THE MAGISTRATE.

Vautier.

A Marriage at Sea

Mr. Higginson nursed his knee and smiled at the deck with a look of embarrassment, though he had been attending to the skipper's words with lawyer-like gravity down to that moment.

. . . .

" I have been thinking over the matter of marriages at sea, Mr. Barclay," he began, with a wary look to make sure that nobody was listening. " I wish we had a copy of the Merchant Shippings Act for 1854, for I believe there is a section which provides that every master of a ship carrying an official log-book shall enter in it every marriage that takes place on board, together with the names and ages of the parties; and I fancy there is another section which provides that every master of every foreign-going ship shall sign and deliver to some mercantile marine authority a list containing, among other things, a statement of every marriage which takes place on board. There is also an act called, if my memory serves me, the Confirmation of Marriage on her Majesty's Ships Act; but this, I presume, does not concern what may happen in merchant vessels. I should like to read up Hammick on the ' Marriage Laws of England.' One thing, however, is clear; marriage at sea is contemplated by the Merchant Shippings Act of 1854. Merchantmen do not carry chaplains : a clergyman in attendance as a passenger was assuredly not in the minds of those who are responsible for the Act. The sections, in my opinion, point to the captain as the person to officiate ; and, having turned the matter thoroughly over, I don't scruple to pronounce that a marriage solemnised at sea by the master of a British merchantman is as legal and valid as though celebrated on shore in the usual way."

" I am delighted to hear you say so," said I.

. . . .

Presently I looked at my watch; a quarter to ten. Mr. Tooth strolled up to me.

" All alone, Mr. Barclay? 'T is a fact, have you noticed, that when a man is about to get married, people hold off from him? I can understand this of a corpse; but a live young man, you know — and only because he's going to get married! By the way, as it is to be a private affair, I suppose there is no chance for *me*?"

"The captain is the host," I answered. "He is to play the father. If he chooses to invite you, by all means be present." As I spoke, the captain came on deck, turning his head about in manifest search of me. He gravely beckoned with an air of ceremony, and Mr. Tooth and I went up to him. He looked at Mr. Tooth, who immediately said, —

"Captain, a wedding at sea is good enough to remember — something for a man to talk about. *Can't* I be present?" And he dropped his head on one side with an insinuating smile.

"No, sir," answered Captain Parsons, with true sea-grace, and, putting his hand on my arm, he carried me right aft. "The hour's at hand," said he. "Who's to be present, d'ye know? for if it's to be private we don't want a crowd."

"Mrs. Barstow and Miss Moggadore; nobody else, I believe."

"Better have a couple of men as witnesses. What d'ye say to Mr. Higginson?"

"Anybody you please, captain."

"And the second?" said he, tilting his hat and thinking. "McCosh? Yes, I don't think you can do better than McCosh. A thoughtful Scotchman, with an excellent memory." He pulled out his watch. "Five minutes to ten. Let us go below." And down he went.

The steward was despatched to bring Mr. Higginson and the chief mate, Mr. McCosh, to the captain's cabin. The saloon was empty; possibly out of consideration to our feelings, the people had gone on deck or withdrawn to their berths.

"Bless me! I had quite forgotten," cried Captain Parsons, as he entered his cabin. "Have you a wedding ring, Mr. Barclay?"

"Oh, yes," I answered, laughing, and pulling out the purse in which I kept it. "Little use in sailing away with a young lady, Captain Parsons, to get married, unless you carry the ring with you."

"Glad you have it. We can't be too shipshape. But I presume you know," said the little fellow, "that any sort of a ring would do — even a curtain-ring. No occasion for the lady to wear what you slip on, though I believe it's expected she should keep it upon her finger till the service is over. Let me see now — there's something else I wanted to say. Oh, yes; who's to give the bride away?"

There was a knock at the door, and Mr. Higginson, followed by Mr. McCosh, entered.

"Mr. Higginson," immediately cried the captain, "you will give the bride away."

The lawyer put his hand upon his shirt-front, and bowed. I glanced at McCosh, who had scarcely had time to do more than flourish a hair-brush. He was extraordinarily grave, and turned a very literal eye round about. I asked him if he had ever before taken part in a ceremony of this sort at sea. He reflected, and answered, "No, neither at sea nor ashore."

"But, seeing that you are a witness, Mr. McCosh, you thoroughly understand the significance of the marriage service, I hope?" said Mr. Higginson, drily.

"D'ye know, then, sir," answered McCosh, in the voice of a saw going through a balk of timber, "I never read or heard a line of the marriage service in all my life. But I have a very good understanding of the object of the ceremony."

"I hope so, Mr. McCosh," said the captain, looking at him doubtfully. "It is as a witness that you're here."

"'T will be a *fact*, no doubt?" said Mr. McCosh.

"Certainly," said the lawyer.

"Then, of course," said the mate, "I shall always be able to swear to it."

"Ten minutes past ten," cried the captain, whipping out his watch. "I hope Miss Moggadore's not keeping the ladies waiting while she powders herself or fits a new cap to her hair."

He opened the door to call to the steward, then hopped back with a sudden convulsive sea-bow to make room for the ladies, who were approaching.

My darling was very white and looked at me piteously. She came to my side, and slipped her hand into mine, whispering under her breath, " Such a silly, senseless ceremony ! " I pressed her fingers, and whispered back that the ceremony was not for us, but for Aunt Amelia. She wore her hat and jacket, and Mrs. Barstow was clad as for the deck ; but Miss Moggadore, on the other hand, as though in justification of what the captain had said about her, made her appearance in the most extraordinary cap I had ever seen, — an inflated arrangement, as though she were fresh from a breeze of wind that held it bladder-like. She had changed her gown, too, for a sort of Sunday dress of satin or some such material. She courtesied on entering, and took up her position alongside of McCosh, where she stood viewing the company with an austere gaze which so harmonised with the dry, literal, sober stare of the mate that I had to turn my back upon her to save the second explosion of laughter.

" Are we all ready ? " said the little captain, in the voice of a man who might hail his mate to tell him to prepare to put the ship about, and McCosh mechanically answered :

" Ay, ay, sir, all ready."

On this the captain went to the table, where lay a big church service in large type, and, putting on his glasses, looked at us over them as a hint for us to take our places. He then began to read, so slowly that I foresaw, unless he skipped many of the passages, we should be detained half the morning in his cabin. He read with extraordinary enjoyment of the sound of his own voice, and constantly lifted his eyes, while he delivered the sentences as though he were admonishing instead of marrying us. Grace kept her head hung, and I felt her trembling when I took her hand. I had flattered myself that I should exhibit no nervousness in such an ordeal as this; but, though I was not sensible of any disposition to tears, I must confess that my secret agitation was incessantly prompting me to laughter of a hysterical sort, which I restrained with struggles that caused me no small suffering. It is at such times as these, perhaps, that the imagination is most inconveniently active.

The others stood behind me; I could not see them; it would have eased me, I think, had I been able to do so. The thought of McCosh's face, the fancy of Miss Moggadore's cap, grew dreadfully oppressive through my inability to vent the emotions they induced. My distress was increased by the mate's pronunciation of the word "Amen." He was always late with it, as though waiting for the others to lead the way, unless it was that he chose to take a "thocht" before committing himself. My wretchedness was heightened by the effect of this lonely Amen, whose belatedness he accentuated by the fervent manner in which he breathed it out.

Yet, in spite of the several grotesque conditions which entered into it, this was a brief passage of experience that was by no means lacking in romantic and even poetic beauty. The flashful trembling of the sunlit sea was in the atmosphere of the cabin, and bulkhead and upper deck seemed to race with the rippling of the waves of light in them. Through the open port came the seething and pouring song of the ocean, — the music of smiting billows, the small harmonies of foam-bells and of seething eddies. There was the presence of the ocean, too, the sense of its infinity, and of the speeding ship, a speck under the heavens, yet fraught with the passions and feelings of a multitude of souls bound to a new world, fresh from a land which many of them would never again behold.

The captain took a very long time in marrying us. Had this business possessed any sort of flavour of sentiment for Grace, it must have vanished under the slow, somewhat husky, self-complacent, deep-sea delivery of old Parsons. I took the liberty of pulling out my watch as a hint, but he was enjoying himself too much to be in a hurry. Nothing, I believe, could have so contributed to the felicity of this man as the prospect of uniting one or more couples every day. On several occasions his eyes appeared to fix themselves upon Miss Moggadore, to whom he would accentuate the words he pronounced by several nods. The marriage service, as we all know, is short, yet Captain Parsons kept us an hour in his cabin listening to it. Before reciting " All ye that are married," he hemmed loudly, and appeared to address himself exclusively to Miss Moggadore, to judge by the direction in which he continued to nod emphatically.

At last he closed his book, slowly gazing at one or the other of us over his glasses, as if to witness the effect of his reading in our faces. He then opened his official log-book, and in a whisper, as though he were in church, called Mr. Higginson and Mr. McCosh to the table to witness his entry. Having written it, he requested the two witnesses to read it. Mr. McCosh pronounced it " arl reet," and Mr. Higginson nodded as gravely as though he were about to read a will.

" The ladies must see this entry, too," said Captain Parsons, still preserving his Sabbatical tone. " Can't have too many witnesses. Never can tell what may happen."

The ladies approached and peered, and Miss Moggadore's face took on an unusually hard and acid expression as she pored upon the captain's handwriting.

" Pray read it out, Miss Moggadore," said I.

" Ay, do," exclaimed the captain.

In a thin, harsh voice, like the cheep of a sheave set revolving in a block, — wonderfully in accord, by the way, with the briny character of the ceremony, — the lady read as follows : —

10 : 10 A. M. — Solemnised the nuptials of Herbert Barclay, Esquire, gentleman, and Grace Bellassys, spinster. Present, Mrs. Barstow, Miss Moggadore, James Higginson, Esquire, solicitor, and

A Marriage at Sea

Donald McCosh, chief officer. This marriage thus celebrated was conducted according to the rites and ceremonies of the Church of England.

"And now, Mr. Barclay," said Captain Parsons, as Miss Moggadore concluded, "you'd like a certificate under my hand, would n't you?"

"We're not strangers to Mr. and Mrs. Barclay's views," said Mr. Higginson, "and I am certainly of opinion, captain, that Mr. Barclay ought to have such a certificate as you suggest, that on his arrival at home he may send copies of it to those whom it concerns."

At the utterance of the words "Mr. and Mrs. Barclay" I laughed, while Grace started, gave me an appealing look, turned a deep red, and averted her face. The captain produced a sheet of paper, and, after looking into a dictionary once, — "Nothing like accuracy," said he, "in jobs of this sort," — he asked, "Will this do?" and thereupon read as follows:

Ship "Carthusian,"
At Sea [such and such a date].

I, Jonathan Parsons, master of the above-named ship "Carthusian," of London, toward New Zealand, do hereby certify that I have this day united in the holy bonds of wedlock, the following persons, to-wit: Herbert Barclay, Esquire, and Grace Bellassys, spinster, in the presence of the undersigned.

"Nothing could be better," said I.

"Now, gentlemen and ladies," said the captain, "if you will please sign your names."

This was done, and the document handed to me. I pocketed it with a clear sense of its value, — as regards, I mean, the effect I might hope it would produce on Lady Amelia Roscoe. Captain Parsons and the others then shook hands with us, the two ladies kissing Grace, who, poor child, looked exceedingly frightened and pale.

"What's the French word for breakfast?" asked Captain Parsons.

" *Dejewner*, sir," answered McCosh.

Parsons bent his ear with a frown. " You 're giving me the Scotch for it, I believe," cried he.

" It 's *déjeûner*, I think," said I, scarce able to speak for laughing.

" Ay, that 'll be it," cried the captain. " Well, as Mr. and Mrs. Barclay don't relish the notion of a public *degener*, we must drink their healths in a bottle of champagne."

He put his head out of the cabin, and called to the steward, who brought the wine, and for hard upon half an hour my poor darling and I had to listen to speeches from old Parsons and the lawyer. Even McCosh must talk. In slow and rugged accents he invited us to consider how fortunate we were in having fallen into the hands of Captain Parsons. Had *he* been master of the " Carthusian," there could have been no marriage, for he would not have known what to do. He had received a valuable professional hint that morning, and he begged to thank Captain Parsons for allowing him to be present on so interesting an occasion.

This said, the proceedings ended. Mrs. Barstow, passing Grace's hand under her arm, carried her off to her cabin, and I, accepting a cigar from the captain's box, went on deck to smoke it, and to see if there was anything in sight likely to carry us home.

Married ! Could I believe it ? If so — if I was indeed a wedded man — then I suppose never in the annals of love-making could anything stranger have happened than that a young couple eloping from a French port should be blown out into the ocean and there united, not by a priest, but by a merchant skipper.

From "THE BUILDING OF THE SHIP"[1]

By HENRY WADSWORTH LONGFELLOW

ALL is finished! and at length
    Has come the bridal day
Of beauty and of strength.
To-day the vessel shall be launched!
With fleecy clouds the sky is blanched,
And o'er the bay,
Slowly, in all his splendours dight,
The great sun rises to behold the sight.

. . . .

There she stands,
With her foot upon the sands,
Decked with flags and streamers gay,
In honour of her marriage day,
Her snow-white signals fluttering, blending,
Round her like a veil descending.
Ready to be
The bride of the gray old sea.

On the deck another bride
Is standing by her lover's side.
Shadows from the flags and shrouds,
Like the shadows cast by clouds,
Broken by many a sunny fleck,
Fall around them on the deck.

The prayer is said,
The service read,
The joyous bridegroom bows his head;
And in tears the good old Master

1 *By special permission of Houghton, Mifflin & Co.*

Shakes the brown hand of his son,
Kisses his daughter's glowing cheek
In silence, for he cannot speak,
And ever faster
Down his own the tears begin to run.
The worthy pastor —
The shepherd of that wandering flock,
That has the ocean for its wold,
That has the vessel for its fold,
Leaping ever from rock to rock —
Spake, with accents mild and clear,
Words of warning, words of cheer,
But tedious to the bridegroom's ear.

The Minister's Wooing

From "THE MINISTER'S WOOING"[1]

By HARRIET BEECHER STOWE

MY DEAR SISTER, — You wonder, I s'pose, why I have n't written you ; but the fact is, I 've been run just off my feet, and worked till the flesh aches, so it seems as if it would drop off my bones, with this wedding of Mary Scudder's. And, after all, you will be astonished to hear that she ha'n't married the Doctor, but that Jim Marvyn that I told you about. You see he came home a week before the wedding was to be, and Mary, she was so conscientious she thought 't wa'n't right to break off with the Doctor, and so she was for going right on with it ; and Mrs. Scudder, she was for going on more yet ; and the poor young man, he could n't get a word in edgeways, and there would n't anybody tell the Doctor a word about it, and there 't was drifting along, and both on 'em feeling dreadful, and so I thought to myself, " I 'll just take my life in my hand, like Queen Esther, and go in and tell the Doctor all about it." And so I did. I 'm scared to death always when I think of it. But that dear blessed man, he took it like a saint. He just gave her up as serene and calm as a psalm-book, and called Jim in and told him to take her.

Jim was fairly overcrowed, — it really made him feel small, — and he says he 'll agree that there is more in the Doctor's religion than most men's : which shows how important it is for professing Christians to bear testimony in their works, — as I was telling Cerinthy Ann Twitchel ; and she said there wa'n't anything made her want to be a Christian so much, if that was what religion would do for people.

<hr>

[1] *By special permission of Houghton, Mifflin & Co.*

7

97

Well, you see when this came out, it wanted just three days of the wedding, which was to be Thursday, and that wedding dress I told you about, that had lilies of the valley on a white ground, was pretty much made, except puffing the gauze around the neck, which I do with white satin piping-cord, and it looks beautiful too; and so Mrs. Scudder and I, we were thinking 't would do just as well, when in come Jim Marvyn, bringing the sweetest thing you ever saw, that he had got in China, and I think I never did see anything lovelier. It was a white silk, as thick as a board, and so stiff that it would stand alone, and overshot with little fine dots of silver, so that it shone when you moved it, just like frostwork; and when I saw it, I just clapped my hands, and jumped up from the floor, and says I, " If I have to sit up all night, that dress shall be made, and made well, too." For, you know, I thought I could get Miss Olladine Hocum to run the breadths and do such parts, so that I could devote myself to the fine work. And that French woman I told you about, she said she 'd help, and she 's a master-hand for touching things up. There seems to be work provided for all kinds of people, and French people seem to have a gift in all sorts of dressy things, and 't is n't a bad gift either.

Well, as I was saying, we agreed that this was to be cut open with a train, and a petticoat of just the palest, sweetest, loveliest blue that ever you saw, and gauze puffings down the edgings each side, fastened in, every once in a while, with lilies of the valley; and 't was cut square in the neck, with puffings and flowers to match, and then tight sleeves, with full ruffles of that old Mechlin lace that you remember Mrs. Katy Scudder showed you once in that great camphor-wood trunk.

Well, you see, come to get all things together that were to be done, we concluded to put off the wedding till Tuesday; and Madame de Frontignac, she said she would dress the best room for it herself, and she spent nobody knows what time in going round and getting evergreens, and making wreaths, and putting up green boughs over the pictures,

The Departure from Home.

so that the room looked just like the Episcopal Church at Christmas. In fact, Mrs. Scudder said, if it had been Christmas, she should n't have felt it right, but, as it was, she did n't think anybody would think it any harm.

Well, Tuesday night, I and Madame de Frontignac, we dressed Mary ourselves, and, I tell you, the dress fitted as if it was grown on her; and Madame de Frontignac, she dressed her hair; she had on a wreath of lilies of the valley, and a gauze veil that came a'most down to her feet, and came all around her like a cloud, and you could see her white shining dress through it every time she moved, and she looked just as white as a snow-berry, but there were two little pink spots that kept coming and going in her cheeks that kind of lightened up when she smiled, and then faded down again. And the French Lady put a string of real pearls round her neck, and a cross of pearls, which went down and lay hid in her bosom.

She was mighty calm-like while she was being dressed; but just as I was putting in the last pin, she heard the rumbling of a coach downstairs, for Jim Marvyn had got a real elegant carriage to carry her over to his father's in, and so she knew he was to come. And pretty soon Mrs. Marvyn came in the room, and when she saw Mary, her brown eyes kind of danced, and she lifted up both hands, to see how beautiful she looked. And Jim Marvyn, he was standing at the door, and they told him it was n't proper that he should see till the time comes; but he begged so hard that he might just have one peep, that I let him come in, and he looked at her as if she was something he would n't dare to touch; and he says to me softly, says he, "I'm 'most afraid she has got wings somewhere that will fly away from me, or that I shall wake up and find it is a dream."

Well, Cerinthy Ann Twitchel was the bridesmaid, and she came next with the young man she is engaged to. It is all out now, that she is engaged, and she don't deny it. And Cerinthy, she looked handsomer than I ever saw her, in a white brocade, with rosebuds on it, which I guess she got in reference to the future, for they say she is going to be married next month.

Well, we all filled up the room pretty well till Mrs. Scudder came in to tell us that the company were all together; and then they took hold of arms, and they had a little time practising how they must stand, and Cerinthy Ann's beau would always get on the wrong side, 'cause he's rather bashful, and don't know very well what he's about; and Cerinthy Ann declared she was afraid that she would laugh out in prayer-time, 'cause she always did laugh when she knew she mus'n't. But finally Mrs. Scudder told us we must go in, and looked so reproving at Cerinthy that she had to hold her mouth with her pocket-handkerchief.

Well, the old Doctor was standing there in the very silk gown that the ladies gave him to be married in himself, — poor, dear man! — and he smiled kind of peaceful on 'em when they came in, and walked up to a kind of bower of evergreens and flowers that Madame de Frontignac had fixed for them to stand in. Mary grew rather white, as if she was going to faint; but Jim Marvyn stood up just as firm, and looked as proud and handsome as a prince, and he kind of looked down at her, — 'cause, you know, he is a great 'eal taller, — kind of wondering, as if he wanted to know if it were really so. Well, when they got all placed, they let the doors stand open, and Cato and Candace came and stood in the door. And Candace had on her great splendid Mogadore turban, and a crimson and yellow shawl, that she seemed to take comfort in wearing, although it was pretty hot.

Well, so when they were all fixed, the Doctor, he begun his prayer, — and as 'most all of us knew what a great sacrifice he had made, I don't believe there was a dry eye in the room; and when he had done, there was a great time, — people blowing their noses and wiping their eyes, as if it had been a funeral. Then Cerinthy Ann, she pulled off Mary's glove pretty quick; but that poor beau of hers, he made such work of James's that he had to pull it off himself, after all, and Cerinthy Ann, she liked to have laughed out loud. And so when the Doctor told them to join hands, Jim took hold of Mary's hand as if he did n't mean to let go very soon, and so they were married.

I was the first one that kissed the bride after Mrs. Scudder, — I got that promise out of Mary when I was making the dress, and Jim Marvyn, he insisted upon kissing me, — " 'Cause," says he, " Miss Prissy, you 're looking as young and handsome as any of 'em;" and I told him he was a saucy fellow, and I 'd box his ears, if I could reach them.

That French lady looked lovely, dressed in pale pink silk, with long pink wreaths of flowers in her hair; and she came up and kissed Mary and said something to her in French.

And after a while old Candace came up, and Mary kissed her; and then Candace put her arms around Jim's neck, and gave him a real hearty smack, so that everybody laughed.

And then the cake and the wine was passed around, and everybody had good times till we heard the nine-o'clock-bell ring. And then the coach came up to the door, and Mrs. Scudder, she wrapped Mary up, kissing her and crying over her, while Mrs. Marvyn stood stretching her arms out of the coach after her. And then Cato and Candace went after in the wagon behind, and so they all went off together; and ever since then we ha'n't any of us done much but rest, for we were pretty much beat out. So no more at present, from your Affectionate Sister,

PRISSY.

From " BY CELIA'S ARBOR "[1]

By WALTER BESANT and JAMES RICE.

I HAVE come to the end of my story, the only story I have to tell from my own experience. How should it end but with a wedding? There is no romance where there is no love; there is no pleasure in the contemplation of love, unless it ends happily, and is crowned with orange blossoms; love is the chief happiness of life, as everybody knows — except, perhaps, John Pontifex — and has ever been completed by the wedding bells.

Ring, wedding bells, then; shake out the clashing music of your joy over all the fields, startle the farmer at his work, rouse the student at his desk, strike on the ear of the sailor out at sea, echo along the shore, mingle with the roar of the saluting guns to greet the ship's crew when they come home, so that they may know that during their three years' cruise the world's happiness has not altogether died away. Bring back to the old the memory of a day long gone by. Lift up the heart of the young with hope. Put ambitious thoughts of such a day of victory into the mind of the maiden who would like nothing better than to hear the bells ring for herself on such a wedding morning and walk in such a procession, decked with such white robes and such orange wreaths. May they ring for every one of our girls, so that not one shall miss the love of a man but those who are unworthy!

They were married in the old church, the parish church, a mile from the town.

It is a day at the end of October, a breezy day of autumn; the clouds are driving across the sky, light clouds which leave plenty of clear blue sky and sunshine; the leaves are

1 *Published by Harper & Brothers, New York.*

HEALTH TO THE BRIDE.
Erdmann.

lying all about the old churchyard, drifting in heaps against the headstones and whirling round and round like unquiet spirits within the iron railings of the vaults.

The churchyard is full of people waiting to see the wedding; the honest folk from Victory Row are there. I shake hands with Jem Hex and his wife, and half a dozen more, who knew me in the old days of Mrs. Jeram's guardianship. They care less for the bride than for the bridegroom, these denizens of Victory Row. That a boy, so to speak, who used to run ragged about the logs on the Hard, who played on their own doorsteps, who was accustomed to fight Moses daily, and on small provocation, before the sight of all; who actually, only the other day, did not disdain to remember the old time, and cowhided Moses again at the Blue Anchor, — that such a boy should have become such a man was not, of course, unexpected, because out of Victory Row have come plenty of distinguished men, — though not put down in books, — Nelson's bull-dogs, mind you, and a few of Wellington's veterans. But that he should have developed to that height of greatness as to be a real captain in the army, and come home to marry nothing short of the daughter of the mayor, and her a lady as beautiful as the day, that was, if you please, something quite out of the common.

Here is the captain, marching up the walk in uniform and epaulets, as becomes a great occasion. Fall back, good people, don't crowd the captain. God bless the captain! Is the captain looking well to-day ? And a happy day for him, too, if all 's true that 's said. Which, if any credit is due to anybody for that boy turning out so well, it 's due to the captain. There was only one captain for these people. Other persons held equal rank in the navy, it is true ; there were, for instance, Captain Luff, Captain Hardaport, Captain Bobstay — who was only a retired master with captain's title — all living not far from Victory Row ; but they had their names assigned to them as well as their titles, ours had not. The old man, pleased to see so many people gathered together to do honour to him and his, stops, and has a word to say to every one, and then goes on to the church, where he stands by the altar and waits.

The Rev. John Pontifex and Mrs. Pontifex his wife. The sailor-folk know nothing of them except as residents. So they pass in the silence of respect, — John Pontifex, with his long-tail coat on, and a very, very voluminous white muffler around his neck.

The Rev. Verney Broughton. He it is who is going to marry them. Ah! quoth Jem Hex, and a right sort, too, as he has heard, either for a glass of wine, or for a marriage, or for a sermon. From Oxford College he is, and once taught Master Leonard a mort o' learning, which, no doubt, helped him ag'in them Rooshans.

Among the people, bustling here and there with importance, is the historiographer, Ferdinand Brambler, note-book in hand. He goes into the church; comes out and dashes down observations in his note-book on a tombstone; listens to the people and jots down more observations; and then, absorbed in meditation, is seen standing motionless, as if grappling for the mastery of language. This is a great day for Ferdinand.

Round the church-door are all the younger members of the Brambler family, told off to strew flowers at the feet of the bride. Augustus is with them, bearing in his hands a pair of new white cotton gloves, with an air of immense dignity. These crowds, this ringing of bells, strewing of flowers, and general excitement, all attest, in his eyes, to the greatness and glory of the Legal. Nothing in the Scholastic, not even a prize-giving, ever came near it. All the children are dressed in new clothes presented by the captain, so that they may do fitting honour to the occasion.

Leonard had pressed me to be his best man, which, indeed, was my proper place. But I wanted to play the organ for Celia's marriage, and I had promised myself to play my own love-symphony, which she alone knew. It was a fancy of mine. Forty-Four, my faithful little ally and friend, begged to come with me to the organ-loft.

It was after eleven, and time to go up the stairs. What

are all those heavy heels tramping up the aisle ? They are
Leonard's Company, with, I believe, about half the regiment, come to see Gentleman Jack married. I remember
the faces of the rogues; they were at the Blue Anchor that
night when he thrashed Moses, and made him give up the
papers. Jem, the organ-blower, is in his place; Forty-
Four is by me to turn over the leaves. Stay one moment,
Forty-Four, let's look through the curtains again. There
is Leonard going up the aisle. He is in uniform, as are
his best men, as officers of the garrison, the young naval
officer whom they call Griff, and a man of his own regiment. A brave show of scarlet and gold. His brother
officers are mostly in the church, the Colonel among them.

"Here comes Uncle Ferdinand," says Forty-Four.
"Oh, how beautifully he will describe it!"

All are there but the bride. She is coming. Now,
Forty-Four, for Celia's symphony.

The music rolls in echoes among the rafters in the roof.
As I play, I am a prophet, and see before me the happy
years unfold their golden wings. All is as it ought to be;
let those who have to sit during their lives outside the
halls of human joy take pleasure in the prospect of others'
happiness, and be thankful that they can at least look on.

"There is the bride," whispered Forty-Four. "Oh,
how lovely! Oh, how sweet she looks!"

My wedding-hymn of prayer and praise — listen to it,
Celia — I know you are listening — as you stand for a
moment before the altar beside your lover waiting for the
words to be spoken. Listen! there is no joy, says the
music, given to men and women like the holy joy of
love; there can be no praise too full and deep for the
gift of love; there can be no prayer more eloquent than
the prayer for the continuance of love. Listen! it is the
voice of your heart speaking in the music, which rings
and rolls about the pillars of the old church — I learned
it reading in your heart itself — it is singing aloud to God
in gratitude and praise, singing in the music where I have
enshrined and preserved it for you.

I finish my symphony and the service begins. The words are faint and low as they mount to the organ-loft. I have pulled the curtains aside, and we watch, we three, Forty-Four, Jem the organ-blower, and I, from the gallery, while Leonard holds Celia's hand in his, and they take the vow which binds them for ever to each other. You are crying, Forty-Four? Foolish child!

All is over, and they have gone into the vestry. Come, we have played Celia's symphony before the wedding with her hymn. Now for the march. Mendelssohn alone has reached the true, triumphal rapture. His music is the exaltation of the bridegroom; it is a man's song, — the song of a man who bears his bride away; the song of the young men who clap their hands; the jubilant blare of clarions and trumpets, which throw their music abroad to the winds that envious men may hear; and though the women cry, like foolish little Forty-Four, we drown their tears with song and shout. A bridegroom's song of triumph, this.

But the bride is gone, and the bridal company with her; the children have strewed their flowers upon the ground; the carriages have driven off; only the people are left; they, too, are leaving the church; in a few moments we shall be alone in the loft.

Consummatum est. Leonard has come home; Leonard has won his bride; Celia has gone from us. Shut up the organ, Forty-Four; let us go down and join the wedding guests. Somehow, I do not feel much like feasting.

. . . .

Mr. Tyrrell was by no means the kind of man to make a mean show on this auspicious occasion. He had a marquee erected in his garden, where two tables were laid; he invited to the breakfast his whole staff of clerks, with their families, including all who bore the name of Brambler — they had the second table. He would have invited all the regiment if Leonard had allowed him. As it was, there appeared a great gathering of his brother-officers.

By Celia's Arbor

No nobler wedding-breakfast, Ferdinand Brambler reported, had ever before been witnessed in the town, and it reflected, he said, the greatest credit on Mr. Honeybun, the eminent local confectioner and pastrycook, who evinced on this occasion talents of an order inferior to none, not even Fortnum and Mason, the purveyors of princes. It may be mentioned that the occasion was one of which Ferdinand made four columns and a half. The wedding report ran to the butcher's bill for three whole weeks, and included a small outstanding account with the greengrocer, as Augustus himself told me. It was headed " Wedding of the Mayor's Only Daughter," in large type, and was divided into headed sections, thus: " The Churchyard; " " Decorations of the Church; " " The Organist; " — of whom he spoke with some reticence, for Ferdinand had feeling for my long friendship with bride and bridegroom; " The Bridegroom and his Gallant Supporters; " " The Arrival of the Bride; " " The Wedding," in which he gave the rein to religious feelings, and spoke of the impressive reading of Mr. Broughton, the reverent attention of those war-stained heroes, the officers of the regiment, and the tears of the bridesmaids; " The Departure," in which my own rendering of the " Wedding March " was gracefully alluded to; and, finally, " The Wedding Breakfast," in the description of which he surpassed himself, so that those who read of that magnificent feed went hungry immediately. I do not know what reward he received of Mr. Honeybun, the confectioner, but he ought to have had free run among the tarts for life.

It was not at all a solemn or a tearful meal. Mr. John Pontifex, seated well out of his wife's sight, was between two young officers, to whom he communicated recollections of his early life at Oxford, and the reckless profligacy which he had witnessed, and even — " Oh! " I heard him say, " it is a most Awful event to look back upon " — participated in and encouraged. He told them the Goose story, he told how he had once fallen in love with a young person — in fact, of the opposite sex — in Oxford, and how, excepting that single experience, "Love," as he said, "has never yet, I regret to say, reached this poor — cold — heart of mine."

All this was very delightful to his two hearers, and I observed the rapture with which they plied him with champagne, of which he drank immense quantities, becoming frightfully pale, and listened to his reminiscences. No doubt, Mrs. Pontifex would have been greatly pleased had she been present that evening in the mess-room, and heard the reproduction of these anecdotes.

It was in the ponderous manner peculiar to clergymen of his standing and scholarship that Mr. Broughton proposed the health of the bride and bridegroom. He had known them both, he said, from infancy. There were no words at his command strong enough to express his affection for the bride, or, if he might say so as a Christian man, his envy of the bridegroom. On the other hand, for such a bride, there was none fitter than such a bridegroom. This young Achilles, having obtained from the Gods a better fate than the hero to whom he likened him, had returned victorious from the wars and won the fairest prize. They all knew Leonard Copleston's history, how the young gentleman, the son of a long line of gallant gentlemen, met adverse Fortune with a resolute front, and conquered her, not with a sword, but with a bayonet; what they did not know, perhaps, was what he could tell them, as Leonard's tutor, that he had always as a boy looked on the gallant soldier as the noblest type of manhood.

"We all," said Mr. Broughton, "envy the man who fights; even the most popular priest is the priest militant; the glory of a poet or a painter is pale compared with the glory of a general; let us wish for Leonard Copleston a long career of honour and distinction, and for them both, my friends, for Celia and Leonard Copleston, let us wish that their love may endure beyond the brief moon of passion, and grow in depth as the years run on;

that, in fact, like the finest port, age may only develop its colour, bring out its bouquet, and mature its character ! "

The old captain would not speak, though they drank his health. He had been sitting opposite to Celia, and when they said kind things about him — it was Leonard's colonel who said them — he only got up, and with a breaking voice said he thanked God for the happiest day in all his life.

"THE MARRIAGE CEREMONY"

By WILLIAM WORDSWORTH

THE Vested Priest before the Altar stands;
    Approach, come gladly, ye prepared, in sight
Of God and chosen friends, your troth to plight
With the symbolic ring, and willing hands
Solemnly joined.   Now sanctify the bands,
O Father! — to the Espoused thy blessing give,
That mutually assisted they may live
Obedient, as here taught, to thy commands.
So prays the Church, to consecrate a Vow
" The which would endless matrimony make; "
Union that shadows forth and doth partake
A mystery potent human love to endow
With heavenly, each more prized for the other's sake;
Weep not, meek bride! uplift thy timid brow.

Auld Licht Idylls

From "AULD LICHT IDYLLS"

By J. M. BARRIE

THE natural politeness of the Allardice family gave me my invitation to Tibbie's wedding. I was taking tea and cheese early one wintry afternoon with the smith and his wife, when little Joey Todd in his Sabbath clothes peered in at the passage, and then knocked primly at the door. Andra forgot himself, and called out to him to come in by; but Jess frowned him into silence and, hastily donning her black mutch, received Willie on the threshold. Both halves of the door were open, and the visitor had looked us over carefully before knocking; but he had come with the compliments of Tibbie's mother, requesting the pleasure of Jess and her man that evening to the lassie's marriage with Sam'l Todd, and the knocking at the door was part of the ceremony. Five minutes afterward Joey returned to beg a moment of me in the passage; when I, too, got my invitation. The lad had just received, with an expression of polite surprise, though he knew he could claim it as his right, a slice of crumbling shortbread, and taken his staid departure, when Jess cleared the tea-things off the table, remarking simply that it was a mercy we had not got beyond the first cup. We then retired to dress.

About six o'clock, the time announced for the ceremony, I elbowed my way through the expectant throng of men, women, and children that already besieged the smith's door. Shrill demands of "Toss, toss!" rent the air every time Jess' head showed on the window blind, and Andra hoped, as I pushed open the door, "that I hadna forgotten my bawbees." Weddings were celebrated among the Auld Lichts by showers of ha'pence, and the guests on their way to the bride's house had to scatter to the hungry rabble like housewives feeding poultry. Willie Todd, the best man, who had never come out so strong in his life before, slipped through the back window, while the crowd, led on by Kitty McQueen, seethed in front, and making a bolt for it to the " 'Sosh," was back in a moment with a handful of small change. " Dinna toss ower lavishly at first," the smith whispered me nervously, as we followed Jess and Willie into the darkening wynd.

The guests were packed hot and solemn in Johnny Allardice's " room ; " the men anxious to surrender their seats to the ladies who happened to be standing, but too bashful to propose it ; the ham and the fish frizzling noisily side by side and hissing out every now and then to let all whom it concern know that Janet Craik was adding more water to the gravy. A better woman never lived ; but oh, the hypocrisy of the face that beamed greeting to the guests as if it had nothing to do but politely show them in, and gasped next moment with upraised arms over what was nearly a fall in crockery. When Janet sped to the door, her " splett new " merino dress fell, to the pulling of a string, over her home-made petticoat, like the drop scene in a theatre, and rose as promptly when she returned to slice the bacon. The murmur of admiration that filled the room when she entered with the minister was an involuntary tribute to the spotlessness of her wrapper and a great triumph for Janet. If there is an impression that the dress of the Auld Lichts was on all occasions as sombre as their faces, let it be known that the bride was but one of several in " whites," and that Mag Munn had only at the last moment been dissuaded from wearing flowers. The minister, the Auld Lichts congratulated themselves, disapproved of all such decking of the person and bowing of the head to idols ; but on such an occasion he was not expected to observe it. Bell Whamond, however, has reason for knowing that, marriages or no marriages, he drew the line at curls.

By-and-by Sam'l Todd, looking a little dazed, was pushed into the middle of the room to Tibbie's side, and the minister raised his voice in prayer. All eyes were closed reverently, except perhaps the bridegroom's, which

THE ELOPEMENT.

Delort.

seemed glazed and vacant. It was an open question in the community whether Mr. Dishart did not miss his chance at weddings; the men shaking their heads over the comparative brevity of the ceremony, the women worshipping him (though he never hesitated to rebuke them when they showed it too openly) for the urbanity of his manners. At that time, however, only a minister of such experience as Mr. Dishart's predecessor could lead up to a marriage in prayer without inadvertently joining the couple, and the catechising was mercifully brief. Another prayer followed the union; the minister waived his right to kiss the bride; every one looked at every other one as if he had for the moment forgotten what he was on the point of saying and found it very annoying; and Janet signalled frantically to Willie Todd, who nodded intelligently in reply, but evidently had no idea what she meant. In time Johnny Allardice, our host, who became more and more doited as the night proceeded, remembered his instructions, and led the way to the kitchen, where the guests, having politely informed the hostess that they were not hungry, partook of a hearty tea. Mr. Dishart presided, with the bride and bridegroom near him; but though he tried to give an agreeable turn to the conversation by describing the extensions at the cemetery, his personality oppressed us, and we only breathed freely when he rose to go. Yet we marvelled at his versatility. In shaking hands with the newly married couple the minister reminded them that it was leap-year, and wished them " three hundred and sixty-six happy and God-fearing days."

Sam'l's station being too high for it, Tibbie did not have a penny wedding, which her thrifty mother bewailed, penny weddings starting a couple in life. I can recall nothing more characteristic of the nation from which the Auld Lichts sprang than the penny wedding, where the only revellers that were not out of pocket by it were the couple who gave the entertainment. The more the guests ate and drank the better, pecuniarily, for their hosts. The charge for admission to the penny wedding (practically to the feast that followed it) varied in different districts, but with us it was generally a shilling. Perhaps the penny extra to the fiddler accounts for the name penny wedding. The ceremony having been gone through in the bride's house, there was an adjournment to a barn or other convenient place of meeting, where was held the nuptial feast; long white boards from Rob Angus' sawmill, supported on trestles, stood in lieu of tables; and those of the company who could not find a seat waited patiently against the wall for a vacancy. The shilling gave every guest the free run of the groaning board; but though fowls were plentiful, and even white bread too, little had been spent on them. The farmers of the neighbourhood, who looked forward to providing the young couple with drills of potatoes for the coming winter, made a bid for their custom by sending them a fowl gratis for the marriage supper. It was popularly understood to be the oldest cock of the farmyard, but for all that it made a brave appearance in a shallow sea of soup. The fowls were always boiled, — without exception, so far as my memory carries me; the guid-wife never having the heart to roast them, and so lose the broth. One round of whiskey-and-water was all the drink to which his shilling entitled the guest. If he wanted more he had to pay for it. There was much revelry, with song and dance, that no stranger could have thought these stiff-limbed weavers capable of; and the more they shouted and whirled through the barn, the more their host smiled and rubbed his hands. He presided at the bar improvised for the occasion, and if the thing was conducted with spirit his bride flung an apron over her gown and helped him. I remember one elderly bridegroom who, having married a blind woman, had to do double work at his penny wedding. It was a sight to see him flitting about the torch-lit barn, with a kettle of hot water in one hand and a besom to sweep up crumbs in the other.

Though Sam'l had no penny wedding, however, we made a night of it at his marriage.

Auld Licht Idylls

Wedding-chariots were not in those days, though I know of Auld Lichts being conveyed to marriages nowadays by horses with white ears. The tea over, we formed in couples, and — the best man with the bride, the bridegroom with the best maid, leading the way — marched in slow procession to Tibbie's new home, between lines of hoarse and eager onlookers. An attempt was made by an itinerant musician to head the company with his fiddle; but instrumental music, even in the streets, was abhorrent to sound Auld Lichts, and the minister had spoken privately to Willie Todd on the subject. As a consequence, Peter was driven from the ranks. The last thing I saw that night, as we filed, bareheaded and solemn, into the newly married couple's house, was Kitty McQueen's vigorous arm, in a dishevelled sleeve, pounding a pair of urchins who had got between her and a muddy ha'penny.

That night there was revelry and boisterous mirth (or what the Auld Lichts took for such) in Tibbie's kitchen. At eleven o'clock Davit Lunan cracked a joke. Davie Haggart, in reply to Bell Dundas' request, gave a song of distinctly secular tendencies. The bride (who had carefully taken off her wedding-gown on getting home and donned a wrapper) coquettishly let the bridegroom's father hold her hand. In Auld Licht circles, when one of the company was offered whiskey and refused it, the others, as if pained even at the offer, pushed it from them as a thing abhorred. But Davie Haggart set another example on this occasion, and no one had the courage to refuse to follow it. We sat late round the dying fire, and it was only Willie Todd's scandalous assertion (he was but a boy) about his being able to dance that induced us to think of moving. In the community, I understand, this marriage is still memorable as the occasion on which Bell Whamond laughed in the minister's face.

From "A SCOTTISH COUNTRY WEDDING"

By JAMES GRAHAME

TH' appointed day arrives, a blithesome day
   Of festive jollity; yet not devoid
Of soft regret to her about to leave
A parent's roof, yes, at the word, join hands,
A tear reluctant starts, as she beholds
Her mother's looks, her father's silvery hairs.
But serious thoughts take flight, when from the barn,
Soon as the bands are knit, a jocund sound
Strikes briskly up, and nimble feet beat fast
Upon the earthen floor. Through many a reel
With various steps uncouth, some new, some old,
Some all the dancer's own, with Highland flings
Not void of grace, the lads and lassies strive
To dance each other down; and oft when quite
Forespent, the fingers merrily cracked, the bound,
The rallying shout well-tuned, and sudden change
To sprightlier tune, revive the flagging foot,
And make it feel as if it tripped in air.
   When all are tired and all his stock of reels
The minstrel o'er and o'er again has run,
The cheering flagon circles round; meanwhile,
A soften'd tune, and slower measure flows
Sweet from the strings, and stills the boisterous joy.

  .   .   .   .

   But, light now failing, glimmering candles shine
In ready chandeliers of moulded clay
Stuck round the walls, displaying to the view
The ceiling rich with cobweb drapery hung.
Meanwhile, from mill and smiddy, field and barn,

Fresh groups come hastening in ; but of them all,
The miller bears the gree, as rafter high
He leaps, and, lighting, shakes a dusty cloud all round.
    In harmless merriment, protracted long,
The hours glide by.   At last, the stocking thrown,
And duly every gossip rite performed,
Youths, maids, and matrons take their several ways ;
While drouthy carles, waiting for the moon,
Sit down again, and quaff till daylight dawn.

From "JANE EYRE"

By CHARLOTTE BRONTË

SOPHIE came at seven to dress me; she was very long indeed in accomplishing her task, so long that Mr. Rochester, grown, I suppose, impatient of my delay, sent up to ask why I did not come. She was just fastening my veil (the plain square of blonde after all) to my hair with a brooch; I hurried from under her hands as soon as I could.

"Stop!" she cried in French. "Look at yourself in the mirror; you have not taken one peep."

So I turned at the door: I saw a robed and veiled figure, so unlike my usual self that it seemed almost the image of a stranger.

"Jane!" called a voice, and I hastened down. I was received at the foot of the stairs by Mr. Rochester.

"Lingerer," he said, "my brain is on fire with impatience, and you tarry so long!"

He took me into the dining-room, surveyed me keenly all over, pronounced me "fair as a lily, and not only the pride of his life, but the desire of his eyes," and then telling me he would give me but ten minutes to eat some breakfast, he rung the bell. One of his lately hired servants, a footman, answered it.

"Is John getting the carriage ready?"

"Yes, sir."

"Is the luggage brought down?"

"They are bringing it down now, sir."

"Go you to the church: see if Mr. Wood (the clergyman) and the clerk are there; return and tell me."

The church, as the reader knows, was just beyond the gates. The footman soon returned.

"Mr. Wood is in the vestry, sir, putting on his surplice."

HOME FROM THE HONEYMOON.
Waller.

" And the carriage ? "

" The horses are harnessing."

" We shall not want it to go to church, but it must be
ready the moment we return ; all the boxes and luggage
arranged and strapped on, and the coachman in his seat."

" Yes, sir."

" Jane, are you ready ? "

I rose. There were no groomsmen, no bridesmaids, no
relatives to wait for or marshal; none but Mr. Rochester
and I. Mrs. Fairfax stood in the hall as we passed. I
would fain have spoken to her, but my hand was held by a
grasp of iron; I was hurried along by a stride I could hardly
follow ; and to look at Mr. Rochester's face was to feel
that not a second of delay would be tolerated for any purpose. I wonder what other bridegroom ever looked as he
did — so bent up to a purpose, so grimly resolute ; or who,
under such steadfast brows, ever revealed such flaming and
flashing eyes.

I know not whether the day was fair or foul ; in descending the drive I gazed neither on sky nor earth: my heart
was with my eyes, and both seemed migrated into Mr.
Rochester's frame. I wanted to see the invisible thing on
which, as we went along, he appeared to fasten a glance
fierce and fell. I wanted to feel the thoughts whose force
he seemed breasting and resisting.

At the churchyard wicket he stopped ; he discovered I
was quite out of breath. " Am I cruel in my love ? " he
said. " Delay an instant; lean on me, Jane."

And now I can recall the picture of the gray old house
of God rising calm before me, of a rook wheeling round
the steeple, of a ruddy morning sky beyond. I remember
something, too, of the green grave-mounds ; and I have not
forgotten, either, two figures of strangers, straying among
the low hillocks, and reading the mementos graven on the
few mossy headstones. I noticed them because, as they
saw us, they passed round to the back of the church; and
I doubted not they were going to enter by the side-aisle
door, and witness the ceremony. By Mr. Rochester they

were not observed; he was earnestly looking at my face, from which the blood had, I dare say, momentarily fled; for I felt my forehead dewy, and my cheeks and lips cold. When I rallied, which I soon did, he walked gently with me up the path to the porch.

We entered the quiet and humble temple; the priest waited in his white surplice at the lowly altar, the clerk beside him. All was still; two shadows only moved in a remote corner. My conjecture had been correct; the strangers had slipped in before us, and they now stood by the vault of the Rochesters, their backs toward us, viewing through the rails the old, time-stained, marble tomb, where a kneeling angel guarded the remains of Damon de Rochester, slain at Marston Moor, in the time of the civil wars, and of Elizabeth, his wife.

Our place was taken at the communion-rails. Hearing a cautious step behind me, I glanced over my shoulder; one of the strangers — a gentleman, evidently — was advancing up the chancel. The service began. The explanation of the intent of matrimony was gone through; and then the clergyman came a step further forward, and, bending slightly toward Mr. Rochester, went on.

" I require and charge you both (as ye will answer at the dreadful day of judgment, when the secrets of all hearts shall be disclosed) that if either of you know any impediment why ye may not be lawfully joined together in matrimony, ye do now confess it; for be ye well assured that so many as are coupled together otherwise than God's Word doth allow, are not joined together by God, neither is their matrimony lawful."

He paused, as the custom is. When is the pause after that sentence ever broken by reply? Not, perhaps, once in a hundred years. And the clergyman, who had not lifted his eyes from his book, and had held his breath but for a moment, was proceeding, his hand was already stretched toward Mr. Rochester, as his lips unclosed to ask, " Wilt thou have this woman for thy wedded wife?" when a distinct and near voice said, —

" The marriage cannot go on; I declare the existence of an impediment."

The clergyman looked up at the speaker, and stood mute; the clerk did the same; Mr. Rochester moved slightly, as if an earthquake had rolled under his feet: taking a firmer footing, and not turning his head or eyes, he said, " Proceed."

Profound silence fell when he had uttered that word, with deep but low intonation. Presently Mr. Wood said:

" I cannot proceed without some investigation into what has been asserted, and evidence of its truth or falsehood."

" The ceremony is quite broken off," subjoined the voice behind us. " I am in a condition to prove my allegation; an insuperable impediment to this marriage exists."

Mr. Rochester heard, but heeded not; he stood stubborn and rigid, making no movement but to possess himself of my hand. What a hot and strong grasp he had! — and how like quarried marble was his pale, firm, massive front at this moment! How his eyes shone, still watchful, and yet mild beneath!

Mr. Wood seemed at a loss. " What is the nature of the impediment?" he asked. " Perhaps it may be got over — explained away?"

" Hardly," was the answer. " I have called it insuperable, and I speak advisedly."

The speaker came forward, and leaned on the rails. He continued, uttering each word distinctly, calmly, steadily, but not loudly, —

" It simply consists in the existence of a previous marriage; Mr. Rochester has a wife now living."

.   .   .   .

READER, I married him. A quiet wedding we had; he and I, the parson and clerk, were alone present. When we got back from church, I went into the kitchen of the manor-house, where Mary was cooking the dinner, and John cleaning the knives, and I said, —

" Mary, I have been married to Mr. Rochester this

morning." The housekeeper and her husband were both of that decent phlegmatic order of people, to whom one may at any time safely communicate a remarkable piece of news without incurring the danger of having one's ears pierced by some shrill ejaculation, and subsequently stunned by a torrent of wordy wonderment. Mary did look up, and she did stare at me; the ladle with which she was basting a pair of chickens roasting at the fire, did for some three minutes hang suspended in air; and for the same space of time John's knives also had rested from the polishing process; but Mary, bending again over the roast, said only, —

"Have you, miss? Well, for sure!"

From "PEREGRINE PICKLE"

By TOBIAS SMOLLETT

THE fame of this extraordinary conjunction spread all over the county ; and on the day appointed for their spousals, the church was surrounded by an inconceivable multitude. The commodore, to give a specimen of his gallantry, by the advice of his friend Hatchway, resolved to appear on horseback on the grand occasion, at the head of all his male attendants, whom he had rigged with the white shirts and black caps formerly belonging to his barge's crew ; and he bought a couple of hunters for the accommodation of himself and his lieutenant. With this equipage, then, he set out from the garrison for the church, after having despatched a messenger to apprise the bride that he and his company were mounted. She got immediately into the coach, accompanied by her brother and his wife, and drove directly to the appointed place, where several pews were demolished and divers persons almost pressed to death by the eagerness of the crowd that broke in to see the ceremony performed.

Thus arrived at the altar, and the priest in attendance, they waited a whole half-hour for the commodore, at whose slowness they began to be under some apprehension, and accordingly dismissed a servant to quicken his pace. The valet, having rode something more than a mile, espied the whole troop disposed in a long field, crossing the road obliquely, and headed by the bridegroom and his friend Hatchway, who, finding himself hindered by a hedge from proceeding farther in the same direction, fired a pistol, and stood over to the other side, making an obtuse angle with the line of his former course ; and the rest of the squadron followed his example, keeping always in the rear of each other like a flight of wild geese.

123

Surprised at this strange method of journeying, the messenger came up, and told the commodore that his lady and her company expected him in the church, where they had tarried a considerable time, and were beginning to be very uneasy at his delay; and therefore desired he would proceed with more expedition. To this message Mr. Trunnion replied, —

" Hark ye, brother, don't you see we make all possible speed? Go back, and tell those who sent you, that the wind has shifted since we weighed anchor, and that we are obliged to make very short trips in tacking, by reason of the narrowness of the channel; and that, as we lie within six points of the wind, they must make some allowance for variation and leeway."

" Lord, sir!" said the valet, " what occasion have you to go zigzag in that manner? Do but clap spurs to your horses, and ride straight forward, and I 'll engage you shall be at the church porch in less than a quarter of an hour."

" What! right in the wind's eye?" answered the commodore. " Ahoy! brother, where did you learn your navigation? Hawser Trunnion is not to be taught at this time of day how to lie his course or keep his own reckoning. And as for you, brother, you best know the trim of your own frigate."

The courier, finding that he had to do with people who would not be easily persuaded out of their own opinions, returned to the temple, and made a report of what he had seen and heard, to the no small consolation of the bride, who had begun to discover some signs of disquiet. Composed, however, by this piece of intelligence, she exerted her patience for the space of another half-hour, during which period, seeing no bridegroom arrive, she was exceedingly alarmed; so that all the spectators could easily perceive her perturbation, which manifested itself in frequent palpitations, heart-heavings, and alterations of countenance, in spite of the assistance of a smelling-bottle which she incessantly applied to her nostrils.

Various were the conjectures of the company on this

occasion. Some imagined he had mistaken the place of rendezvous, as he had never been at church since he first settled in that parish; others believed he had met with some accident, in consequence of which his attendants had carried him back to his own house; and a third set, in which the bride herself was thought to be comprehended, could not help suspecting that the commodore had changed his mind.

But all these suppositions, ingenious as they were, happened to be wide of the true cause that detained him, which was no other than this: The commodore and his crew had, by dint of turning, almost weathered the parson's house that stood to windward of the church, when the notes of a pack of hounds unluckily reached the ears of the two hunters which Trunnion and the lieutenant bestrode. These fleet animals no sooner heard the enlivening sound than, eager for the chase, they sprang away all of a sudden, and strained every nerve to partake of the sport, flew across the fields with incredible speed, overleaped hedges and ditches, and carrying everything in their way, without the least regard to their unfortunate riders.

The lieutenant, whose steed had got the heels of the other, finding it would be great folly and presumption in him to keep the saddle with his wooden leg, very wisely took the opportunity of throwing himself off in his passage through a field of rich clover, among which he lay at his ease; and seeing his captain advancing at full gallop, hailed him with the salutation of " What cheer? ho!" The commodore, who was in infinite distress, eying him askance, as he passed, replied with a faltering voice, " Oh, you are safe at an anchor; I wish I was as safe moored."

Nevertheless, conscious of his disabled heel, he would not venture to try the experiment which had succeeded so well with Hatchway, but resolved to stick as close as possible to his horse's back, until Providence should interpose in his behalf. With this view he dropped his whip, and with his right hand laid fast hold on the pummel, contracting every muscle in his body to secure himself in the seat, and grinning most formidably, in consequence of this exertion. In this attitude he was hurried on a considerable way, when all of a sudden his view was comforted by a five-bar gate that appeared before him, as he never doubted that there the career of his hunter must necessarily end.

But, alas! he reckoned without his host. Far from halting at this obstruction, the horse sprang over it with amazing agility, to the utter confusion and disorder of his owner, who lost his hat and periwig in the leap, and now began to think in good earnest that he was actually mounted on the back of the evil one. He repeated what prayers he could recall, his reflection forsook him, his eyesight and all his other senses failed, he quitted the reins, and, fastening by instinct on the mane, was in this condition conveyed into the midst of the sportsmen, who were astonished at the sight of such an apparition.

Neither was their surprise to be wondered at, if we reflect on the figure that presented itself to their view. The commodore's person was at all times an object of admiration : much more so on this occasion, when every singularity was aggravated by the circumstances of his dress and disaster.

He had put on, in honour of his nuptials, his best coat of blue broadcloth, cut by a tailor at Ramsgate, and trimmed with five dozen of brass buttons, large and small ; his breeches were of the same piece, fastened at the knees with large bunches of tape ; his waistcoat was of red plush, lapelled with green velvet, and garnished with vellum holes ; his boots bore an infinite resemblance, both in colour and shape, to a pair of leather buckets ; his shoulder was graced with a broad buff belt, from whence depended a huge hanger with a hilt like that of a backsword ; and on each side of his pummel appeared a rusty pistol, rammed in a case covered with a bearskin. The loss of his tie periwig and laced hat, which were curiosities of the kind, did not at all contribute to the improvement of the picture, but, on the contrary, by exhibiting his bald pate, and the

natural extension of his lanthorn jaws, added to the pecu-
liarity and extravagance of the whole.

Such a spectacle could not have failed of diverting the
whole company from the chase, had his horse thought
proper to pursue a different route, but the beast was too
keen a sporter to choose any other way than that which the
stag followed ; and therefore, without stopping to gratify
the curiosity of the spectators, he in a few minutes out-
stripped every hunter in the field. There being a deep
hollow way betwixt him and the hounds, rather than ride
round about the length of a furlong to a path that crossed
the lane, he transported himself, at one jump, to the un-
speakable astonishment and terror of a waggoner who
chanced to be underneath, and saw this phenomenon fly
over his carriage.

This was not the only adventure he achieved. The stag
having taken to a deep river that lay in his way, every man
directed his course to a bridge in the neighbourhood; but
our bridegroom's courser, despising all such conveniences,
plunged into the stream without hesitation, and swam in a
twinkling to the opposite shore. This sudden immersion
into an element of which Trunnion was properly a native,
in all probability helped to recruit the exhausted spirits of
the rider, who gave some tokens of sensation, by hallooing
aloud for assistance, which he could not possibly receive,
because his horse still maintained the advantage he had
gained, and would not allow himself to be overtaken.

In short, after a long chase that lasted several hours,
and extended to a dozen miles at least, he was the first one
in at the death of the deer, being seconded by the lieutenant's gelding, which, actuated by the same spirit, had,
without a rider, followed his companion's example.

Our bridegroom, finding himself at last brought up, or,
in other words, at the end of his career, took the opportunity of the first pause, to desire the huntsmen would lend
him a hand in dismounting; and was by their condescen-
sion safely placed on the grass, where he sat staring at the
company as they came in, with such wildness of astonish-

ment in his looks, as if he had been a creature of another species, dropped among them from the clouds.

Before they had fleshed the hounds, however, he recollected himself, and seeing one of the sportsmen take a small flask out of his pocket and apply it to his mouth, judged the cordial to be no other than neat Cognac, which it really was! and expressing a desire of participation, was immediately accommodated with a moderate dose, which perfectly completed his recovery.

By this time he and his two horses had engrossed the attention of the whole crowd; while some admired the elegant proportion and uncommon spirit of the two animals, the rest contemplated the surprising appearance of their master, whom before they had only seen *en passant*; and at length one of the gentlemen, accosting him very courteously, signified his wonder at seeing him in such an equipage, and asked him if he had not dropped his companion by the way.

"Why, look ye, brother," replied the commodore, "mayhap you think me an odd sort of a fellow, seeing me in this trim, especially as I have lost part of my rigging; but this here is the case, d'ye see: I weighed anchor from my own house this morning at ten A. M., with fair weather and a favourable breeze at south-southeast, being bound to the next church on the voyage of matrimony; but howsomever, we had not run down a quarter of a league, when the wind, shifting, blowed directly in our teeth; so that we were forced to tack all the way, d'ye see, and had almost beat up within sight of the port, when these horses, which I had bought but two days before, luffed around in a trice, and then refusing the helm, drove away like lightning with me and my lieutenant, who soon came to anchor in an exceeding good berth. As for my own part, I have been carried over rocks and flats and quicksand; among which I have pitched away a special good tie periwig and an iron-bound hat; and at last am got into smooth water and safe riding; but if ever I venture my carcass upon such a crazy craft again, my name is not Hawser Trunnion."

One of the company, struck with his name, which he had often heard, immediately lay hold on his declaration at the close of this singular account; and observing that his horses were very vicious, asked how he intended to return.

"I am resolved to hire a sledge or waggon, for I 'll never cross the back of a horse again."

"And what do you propose to do with these creatures?" said the other, pointing to the hunters; "they seem to have some mettle; but then they are mere colts, and will take a deal of breaking. Methinks this hinder one is shoulder-slipped."

"I wish both their necks were broke," cried the commodore, "though the two cost me forty good yellow-boys."

"Forty guineas!" exclaimed the stranger, who was a squire and a jockey, as well as owner of the pack. "How a man may be imposed upon! Why, these cattle are clumsy enough to go to plough; mind what a flat counter; do but observe how sharp this here one is in the withers; then he's fired in the further fetlock."

In short, this connoisseur in horse-flesh, having discovered in them all the defects which can possibly be found in that species of animals, offered to give him ten guineas for the two, saying he would convert them into beasts of burden. The owner, who, after what had happened, was very well disposed to listen to anything that was said to their prejudice, implicitly believed the truth of the stranger's asseverations, and inveighing wrathfully against the rascal who had taken him in, forthwith struck a bargain with the squire, who paid him instantly for his purchase; in consequence of which he won the plate at the next Canterbury races.

This affair being transacted to the mutual satisfaction of both parties, as well as to the general entertainment of the company, who laughed in their sleeves at the dexterity of their friend, Trunnion was set upon the squire's own horse, and led by his servant in the midst of this cavalcade, which proceeded to a neighbouring village, where they had bespoke dinner, and where our bridegroom found means to provide himself with another hat and wig. With regard to his marriage, he bore his disappointment with the temper of a philosopher; and the exercise he had undergone having quickened his appetite, sat down at table in the midst of his new acquaintance, making a very hearty meal, and moistening every morsel with a draught of the ale, which he found very much to his satisfaction.

Meanwhile Lieutenant Hatchway made shift to hobble to the church, where he informed the company of what had happened to the commodore; and the bride behaved herself with great decency on the occasion, for, as soon as she understood the danger to which her future husband was exposed, she fainted in the arms of her sister-in-law, to the surprise of all the spectators, who could not comprehend the cause of her disorder; and when she was recovered by the application of smelling-bottles, earnestly begged that Mr. Hatchway and Tom Pipes would take her brother's coach, and go in quest of their commander.

This task they readily undertook, being escorted by all the rest of his adherents on horseback; while the bride and her friends were invited to the parson's house, and the ceremony deferred till another occasion.

The lieutenant, steering his course as near the line of direction in which Trunnion went off as the coach-road would permit, got intelligence of his track from one farmhouse to another; for such an apparition could not fail of attracting particular notice; and one of the horsemen, having picked up his hat and wig in the by-path, the whole troop entered the village where he was lodged, about four o'clock in the afternoon. When they understood he was safely housed at the George, they rode up to the door in a body, and expressed their satisfaction in three cheers; which were returned by the company within, as soon as they were instructed in the nature of the salute by Trunnion, who by this time had entered into all the jollity of his new friends, and was indeed more than half seas over. The lieutenant was introduced to all present, as his sworn brother, and had something tossed up for his dinner.

Tom Pipes and the crew were regaled in another room; and a fresh pair of horses being put to the coach, about six in the evening, the commodore, with all his attendants, departed for the garrison, after having shook hands with every individual in the house.

Without any further accident, he was conveyed in safety to his own gate, before nine, and committed to the care of Pipes, who carried him instantly to his hammock, while the lieutenant was driven away to the place where the bride and her friends remained in great anxiety, which vanished when he assured them that his commodore was safe, being succeeded by abundance of mirth and pleasantry at the account he gave of Trunnion's adventure.

Another day was fixed for the nuptials; and, in order to balk the curiosity of idle people, which had given great offence, the parson was prevailed upon to perform the ceremony in the garrison, which all that day was adorned with flags and pendants displayed, and at night illuminated at the direction of Hatchway, who also ordered the patereroes to be fired as soon as the marriage knot was tied. Neither were the other parts of the entertainment neglected by this ingenious contriver, who produced undeniable proofs of his elegance and art in the wedding supper, which had been committed to his management and direction. This genial banquet was composed entirely of sea-dishes : a huge pillaw, consisting of a large piece of beef sliced, a couple of fowls, and half a peck of rice, smoked in the middle of the board; a dish of hard fish swimming in oil appeared at each end, besides being furnished with a mess of that savoury composition known by the name of lob's course, and a plate of salmagundi. The second course displayed a goose of a monstrous magnitude, flanked with two guinea-hens, a pig barbecued, and hock of salt pork in the midst of a pease pudding, a leg of mutton roasted, with potatoes, and another, boiled with yams. The third service was made up with a loin of fresh pork with apple-sauce, a kid smothered with onions, and a terrapin baked in the shell; and last of all, a prodigious sea-pie was presented, with an infinite volume of pancakes and fritters. That everything might be answerable to the magnificence of this delicate feast, he had provided vast quantities of strong beer, flip, rumbo, and burnt brandy, with plenty of Barbadoes water, for the ladies; and hired all the fiddles within six miles, who, with the addition of a drum, bagpipe, and Welch harp, regaled the guests with a most melodious concert.

From "HUMAN LIFE"

By SAMUEL ROGERS

THEN before All they stand, — the holy vow
And ring of gold, no fond illusions now,
Bind her as his.   Across the threshold led,
And every tear kissed off as soon as shed,
His house she enters, — there to be a light,
Shining within, when all without is night ;
A guardian angel o'er his life presiding,
Doubling his pleasures and his cares dividing,
Winning him back when mingling in the throng,
Back from a world we love, alas ! too long,
To fireside happiness, to hours of ease,
Blest with that charm, the certainty to please.
How oft her eyes read his, her gentle mind
To all his wishes, all his thoughts inclined ;
Still subject, — ever on the watch to borrow
Mirth of his mirth and sorrow of his sorrow !
The soul of music slumbers in the shell,
Till waked and kindled by the master's spell,
And feeling hearts — touch them but rightly — pour
A thousand melodies unheard before !

Wedding Day in Literature and Art

From "IN TRUST; OR, DR. BERTRAND'S HOUSEHOLD"[1]

By AMANDA M. DOUGLAS

THE morning was most beautiful — a clear, crisp air; a sky of the peculiar frosty blue, seen only on the finest of winter days; and a sun whose splendour had never been exceeded. Lily was wild with delight. Before breakfast she ran from room to room saying good-bye to nooks and corners that held for her dear memories, both pleasant and sad. Her mamma's face seemed to gleam out — a sweet, yet indistinct vision, something that brought a waft of heaven and the angels. And dear, dear papa! She drew a long, quivering breath. He had carried them upstairs on his broad shoulders, played hide and seek with them through rooms and halls. Here they had all laughed with him on that fatal evening. In the room they had kissed him for the last time — the last time! and then her tears fell fast indeed. A little distance above here, in the cemetery, he lay asleep, waiting for the dawn of the resurrection; beside him, baby Charlie — a dream, a strand of Daisy's life woven in with theirs. Here they had laughed and frolicked with Robert; here Mabel's quiet girlhood had passed, blessed with all that makes life so rich to enjoy. And her own! Oh, the dear old home! the happy household, dividing, straying off into the keeping of others!

She came to the table with a smiling countenance. Her resolute will stood her in good stead this day. She kept them all merry by the force of her own gay spirits, fully resolved to have her day shadowed by no gloom. Archie had returned the night before. After the meal they started for New York.

1 From "In Trust," by Amanda M. Douglas; published by Lee & Shepard.

BEFORE THE WEDDING.
Volcker.

In Trust; or, Dr. Bertrand's Household

Mr. Auchester met them at the ferry with the family carriage. As they were riding up, he glanced at his watch, and whispered to Lily, " It is ten. Only three hours more ; " which called the bright colour to her face.

At Mrs. Suydam's they were greeted by the Rothelan household. Little Alice dressed in her beautiful christening robe to do honour to Aunt Lily's bridal ; Bel, sweet and fair, in her lavender-coloured silk ; Philip, in a sort of merry mood, amusing himself by quoting Katherine and Petruchio to the blushing couple.

There was no break or awkwardness anywhere. Everybody's apparel, to gloves and handkerchief, was in most perfect order and readily found. There was no bustle, no disorder and plenty of time. Indeed, too much, Mr. Auchester thought. The moments lingered unconscionably.

At length the dressing began. Lily's hair, always so beautiful, needed no more artistic hands than Daisy's. The golden ringlets rippled in their silken sheen and softness like a summer sunbeam. And then came the lovely white silk, with its ample flowing skirt and train, its point lace ; the veil, whose filmy folds seemed like a soft cloud, toning down her dazzling radiance, and shutting within the purity and beauty of girlhood. A wreath of orange blossoms and starry jasmine crowned her.

There had previously been a little discussion about Daisy. Since her baby's death she had worn mourning steadily. Richard, in his perplexity, had applied to Mrs. Suydam.

" A deep purple silk will be the prettiest and most suitable for her," the lady answered readily. " There will be nothing in the colour to disturb her. I think she will not object."

The dress had been a gift from Richard. Mrs. Suydam managed the rest. A tiny ruche of illusion at the neck and wrists, and Daisy was lovely indeed, — a pleasing contrast to the tall, elegant women fluttering about the apartment.

Lily went down to the library to be inspected by Mr.

Auchester and Richard. She flushed a little as she thought of the night of the party, when Ulric first twined flowers in her hair, and asked her not to waltz with any one but him.

Both gentlemen gazed at her in admiration. Indeed, it was impossible to do otherwise.

"The carriages!" announced Tessie, running through the hall, bright and childish in her pink silk, and important with the thought of holding Lily's bouquet during the ceremony.

Lily put her hands upon Richard's shoulders. Her lips moved, but no sound came; her eyes sparkled with something besides their own lustrousness.

"I know all," he said gently. "And whatever of pain there may have been in the past, I want you to remember, when you are far away in your new home, that you have given me much joy, much comfort. And in our dear father's place, whose duties I have often failed to perform rightly, I say, God bless you, my darling, for evermore. May His face shine upon you continually."

"O Dick! tender and true. Papa could have been no more patient — could have loved me no better."

He kissed away the tears ready to fall.

The whole party came trooping down the wide stairs. Mr. Suydam gave orders in his courteous fashion, saw that the ladies were well wrapped in shawls, and marshalled them to the carriages. A niece of his, hardly second to Lily in beauty, was to be bridesmaid.

"It's a shame to cover up so much white glory," Ulric said with a laugh; "but it won't do to run the risk of having you shiver with the cold, or look like a ghost."

They then started. The midday sunshine transfigured the winter scene, and imparted a certain warmth to the atmosphere. Arriving at the church, the party lingered a few seconds to disrobe, and pass under Mrs. Suydam's watchful eye.

Ulric bent over Lily until cheek and lip touched

"The last kiss of girlhood," he said.

It brought a bright flush to her face, whose rosy hue hardly died away during the ceremony. She was amazed to find herself so tranquil, listening, answering with solemn joy, being given away by Richard and feeling the ring as it slipped to its place on her finger, — her golden chain, the sign of another's proprietorship.

Their pride in Lily was certainly very pardonable. She was indeed most exquisitely beautiful as she stood there, calm, unconscious of self, yet so thoroughly human and womanly. Mrs. Suydam was glad to show her to her own and Ulric's friends, dowered in her own right with a peerless loveliness no gold could ever buy. And the crowd who gazed felt its wondrous power.

Ulric and Lily knelt to receive the blessing, while the rest stood. After this Mr. Chaloner's hands were folded over both heads, and his voice, ripe to tremulousness with age, repeated the most beautiful and tender of all benedictions: "The Lord bless thee and keep thee; the Lord make his face to shine upon thee, and be gracious unto thee, and give thee peace, both now and evermore."

Before they rose Ulric kissed her. Her husband's first kiss! Lilian Bertrand's seventeen years of girlhood were ended; Lilian Auchester's new life begun. They walked slowly out of church in a spirit of great calm and happiness, — she trustful, clinging; he with a certain manly grandeur and dignity that enhanced the beauty of his face and figure.

Mrs. Suydam, with her characteristic delicacy, had forborne to invite even her most intimate friends to the house. Her own as well as her husband's hospitality was of that high order which never leaves a sense of obligation. And on this last day she gave up the house to them with so cordial a sweetness that each one felt entirely at home. So there was a joyous season of kisses and congratulations after their return. All wanted a special look at Lily, and she had to stand with Mr. Auchester as she did in church.

"After all," said Tessie gravely, glancing at Lily, "I think he is fully as handsome as you;" which frankness was greeted with a peal of laughter.

" Bravo ! " returned Ulric. " That is the first compliment I have had, after all my efforts to render myself elegant as possible. Tessie, if his High Mightiness Count Petropoloswatoski is still unmarried, I will whisper a private word in his ear, and save him for you."

" I won't have such a name ! " was the child's energetic rejoinder.

A summons to luncheon interrupted them. Lily took off her veil and went to the table in her wedding dress, to the great delight of everybody. They had a grand, enjoyable time. Mr. Suydam, as host, was admirable. He drank Lily's health, and showered upon them both wishes grave, gay, and not a few whose comicality elicited much mirth. From the ladies Ulric came in for his full share.

A little time to don travelling attire, to interchange a few of those tender, sisterly words so hard to utter when the heart is full to overflowing. Yet they could hardly realise that Lily was going away for years. It seemed as if in a few weeks she *must* come back to them.

A good-bye to Ann, Martin, and Mrs. Hall, who had come over to witness the wedding. The rest went to the depot on Twenty-seventh Street. And there Ulric found a crowd of literary friends, who had stolen a march upon him, — friends who shook hands in a heartfelt fashion, breathed wishes that would linger like benisons when the blue ocean rolled between them. They glanced at the bride, in her dress of rich, warm brown, not less elegant or graceful than when in church, her beautiful face framed in with white and scarlet, her golden ringlets gleaming with every movement. Her smiles and responses were enchanting. And both were blessed with a " God-speed " from generous hearts.

Lily nodded from the car window, bright and radiant, as they steamed slowly out of the depot. But the face she turned to her husband was flooded with a rain of tears.

FROM "A BALLAD UPON A WEDDING"

BY SIR JOHN SUCKLING

THE BRIDE

HER finger was so small, the ring
  Would not stay on which they did bring—
    It was too wide a peck;
And, to say truth,—for out it must,—
It looked like the great collar—just—
    About our young colt's neck.

Her feet beneath her petticoat,
Like little mice, stole in and out,
    As if they feared the light;
But O, she dances such a way!
No sun upon an Easter day
    Is half so fine a sight.

Her cheeks so rare a white was on,
No daisy makes comparison;
    Who sees them is undone;
For streaks of red were mingled there,
Such as are on a Cath'rine pear,
    The side that's next the sun.

Her lips were red; and one was thin,
Compared to that was next her chin.
    Some bee had stung it newly;
But, Dick, her eyes so guard her face,
I durst no more upon them gaze
    Than on the sun in July.

Her mouth so small, when she does speak,
Thou 'dst swear her teeth her words did break,
    That they might passage get ;
But she so handled still the matter,
They came as good as ours, or better,
    And are not spent a whit.

From "THE CONSPIRATORS"

By ALEXANDRE DUMAS

BATHILDE uttered a low cry, and the regent, who was walking to and fro with his head bent down, raised it, and turned toward Bathilde, who, incapable of making a step in advance, fell on her knees, drew out her letter, and held it toward the regent. The regent had bad sight ; he did not understand what was going on, and advanced toward this woman, who appeared to him in the shade as a white and indistinct form ; but soon in that form he recognised a woman, and, in that woman, a young, beautiful, and kneeling girl.

As to the poor child, in vain she attempted to articulate a prayer. Voice and strength failing her together, she would have fallen if the regent had not held her in his arms.

" Mon Dieu ! mademoiselle," said the regent, on whom the signs of grief produced their ordinary effect, " what is the matter? What can I do for you? Come to this couch, I beg."

" No, monseigneur, it is at your feet that I should be, for I come to ask a boon."

. . . .

" Mademoiselle," replied the regent, " it appears that those who surround you are destined to save me. I am thus twice your debtor. You said you had a boon to ask of me — speak boldly, I listen to you."

" Oh, my God ! " murmured Bathilde, " give me strength."

" Is it, then, a very important and difficult thing that you desire ? "

Monseigneur," said Bathilde, " it is the life of a man who has deserved death."

" Is it the Chevalier d'Harmental ? "

" Alas, monseigneur, it is."

The regent's brow became pensive, while Bathilde, seeing the impression produced by her demand, felt her heart beat and her knees tremble.

" Is he your relation, your ally, your friend ? "

" He is my life, he is my soul, monseigneur ; I love him."

" But do you know that if I pardon him I must pardon all the rest, and that there are some still more guilty than he is ? "

" His life only, monseigneur ; all I ask is that he may live."

" But if I change his sentence to a perpetual imprisonment you will never see him again. What would become of you, then ? " asked the regent.

Bathilde was obliged to support herself by the back of a chair.

" I would enter into a convent, where I could pray the rest of my life for you, monseigneur, and for him."

" That cannot be," said the regent.

" Why not, monseigneur ? "

" Because this very day, this very hour, I have been asked for your hand, and have promised it."

" You have promised my hand, monseigneur ; and to whom ? "

" Read," said the regent, taking an open letter from his desk, and presenting it to the young girl.

" Raoul's writing ! " cried Bathilde ; " what does this mean ? "

" Read," repeated the regent.

And, in a choking voice, Bathilde read the following letter : —

" MONSEIGNEUR, — I have deserved death — I know it, and I do not ask you for life. I am ready to die at the day and hour appointed ; but it depends on your highness to make this death sweeter to me. I love a young girl whom I should have married if I had lived ; grant that she may be my wife before I die. In

A Marriage under the Directory.

Kaemmerer.

leaving her for ever alone and friendless in the world, let me at least have the consolation of giving her the safeguard of my name and fortune. On leaving the church, monseigneur, I will walk to the scaffold. This is my last wish, my sole desire. Do not refuse the prayer of a dying man. RAOUL D'HARMENTAL.

"Oh, monseigneur," said Bathilde, sobbing, "you see that while I thought of him, he thought of me. Am I right not to love him, when he loves me so much?"

"Yes," said the regent; "and I grant his request; it is just; may it, as he says, sweeten his last moments."

"Monseigneur," cried the young girl, "is that all you grant him?"

"You see," said the regent, "he is just; he asks nothing else."

"Oh, it is cruel! it is frightful! to see him again, and lose him directly; his life, monseigneur, his life I beg; and let me never see him again — better so."

"Mademoiselle," said the regent, in a tone which admitted of no reply, and writing some lines on a paper which he sealed, "here is a letter to Monsieur de Launay, the governor of the Bastille; it contains my instructions with regard to the prisoner. My captain of the guards will go with you, and see that my instructions are followed."

"Oh! his life, monseigneur, his life; on my knees, and in the name of Heaven, I implore you."

The regent rang the bell; a valet entered.

"Call Monsieur the Marquis de Lafare," he said.

"Oh, monsieur, you are cruel," said Bathilde, rising; "at least permit me to die with him. We will not be separated, even on the scaffold; we will be together, even in the tomb."

"Monsieur de Lafare, accompany mademoiselle to the Bastille," said the regent. "Here is a letter for Monsieur de Launay, read it with him, and see that the orders it contains are punctually executed."

Then, without listening to Bathilde's last cry of despair, the Duc d'Orleans opened the door of a closet and disappeared.

143

Lafare dragged the young girl away almost fainting, and placed her in one of the carriages always standing in the courtyard of the Palais Royal. During the route Bathilde did not speak; she was cold, dumb, and inanimate as a statue. Her eyes were fixed and tearless, but on arriving at the fortress she started. She fancied she had seen in the shade, in the very place where the Chevalier de Rohan was executed, something like a scaffold. A little further a sentinel cried " Qui vive ! " the carriage rolled over a drawbridge, and drew up at the door of the governor's house. A footman out of livery opened the door, and Lafare gave Bathilde his arm — she could scarcely stand — all her strength had left her when hope left her. Lafare and the valet were obliged almost to carry her to the first floor. M. de Launay was at supper. They took Bathilde into a room to wait, while Lafare went directly to the governor. Ten minutes passed, during which Bathilde had only one idea, — that of the eternal separation which awaited her. The poor girl saw but one thing, — her lover on the scaffold. Lafare re-entered with the governor. Bathilde looked at them with a bewildered air. Lafare approached her, and offering her his arm, —

" Mademoiselle," said he, " the church is prepared, the priest is ready."

Bathilde, without replying, rose and leaned on the arm which was offered her. M. de Launay went first, lighted by two men bearing torches.

As Bathilde entered by one of the side doors, she saw entering by the other the Chevalier d'Harmental, accompanied by Valef and Pompadour. These were his witnesses, as De Launay and Lafare were hers. Each door was kept by two of the French guard, silent and motionless as statues.

The two lovers advanced, Bathilde pale and fainting, Raoul calm and smiling. On arriving before the altar, the chevalier took Bathilde's hand, and both fell on their knees, without having spoken a word.

The altar was lighted only by four wax tapers, which

threw a funereal light over the chapel, already dark, and filled with gloomy recollections.

The priest commenced the ceremony; he was a fine old man with white hair, and whose melancholy countenance showed the traces of his daily functions. He had been chaplain of the Bastille for five-and-twenty years, and had heard many sad confessions, and seen many lamentable events. He spoke to them, not, as usual, of their duties as husband and wife, but of divine mercy and eternal resurrection. At the benediction Bathilde laid her head on Raoul's shoulder; the priest thought she was fainting, and stopped.

"Finish, my father," murmured Bathilde.

The priest pronounced the sacramental words, to which both replied by a "yes," which seemed to unite the whole strength of their souls. The ceremony finished, D'Harmental asked M. de Launay if he might spend his few remaining hours with his wife. M. de Launay replied that there was no objection. Raoul embraced Pompadour and Valef, thanked them for having served as witnesses at his marriage, pressed Lafare's hand, thanked M. de Launay for his kindness to him during his imprisonment, and throwing his arm round Bathilde, led her away by the door through which he had entered. When they reached D'Harmental's room, Bathilde could no longer contain her tears, a despairing cry escaped her lips, and she fell weeping on a chair, where doubtless D'Harmental had often sat, during the three weeks of his captivity, and thought of her. Raoul threw himself at her feet, and tried to console her, but was himself so much moved by her grief that his own tears mingled with hers. This heart of iron melted in its turn, and Bathilde felt at once on her lips the tears and kisses of her lover. They had been about half an hour together when they heard steps approaching the door, and a key turning in the lock. Bathilde started, and pressed D'Harmental convulsively against her heart. Raoul understood the dreadful fear which crossed her mind, and reassured her. It could not be what she dreaded, since the execution was fixed for eight o'clock in the morning, and eleven had only just struck.

It was M. de Launay who appeared.

" Monsieur le Chevalier," said he, " have the kindness to follow me."

" Alone ? " asked D'Harmental, clasping Bathilde in his arms.

" No, with madame," replied the governor.

"Oh! together, Raoul, together! " cried Bathilde, "where they like, so that we are together. We are ready, monsieur, we are ready."

Raoul kissed Bathilde again ; then recalling all his pride, he followed M. de Launay, with a face which showed no trace of the terrible emotion he had experienced. They passed through some ill-lighted corridors, descended a spiral staircase, and found themselves at the door of a tower. This door opened out to a yard, surrounded by high walls, which served as a promenade to those prisoners who were not kept secret. In this courtyard was standing a carriage with two horses, on one of which was a postilion, and they saw, shining in the darkness, the cuirasses of a dozen musketeers. A ray of hope crossed the minds of the two lovers. Bathilde had asked the regent to change Raoul's death into a perpetual imprisonment. Perhaps the regent had granted him this favour. The carriage, ready, doubtless, to conduct him to some State prison, the musketeers destined to escort them, all gave to the supposition an air of reality. They raised their eyes to heaven to thank God for this unexpected happiness. Meanwhile M. de Launay had signed to the carriage to approach; the postilion had obeyed, the door was opened, and the governor, with his head uncovered, held his hand to Bathilde, to assist her into the carriage.

She hesitated an instant, turning uneasily to see that they did not take Raoul away by the other side; but seeing that he was ready to follow her, she got in without resistance. An instant afterward Raoul was sitting by her; the door was closed, and both carriage and escort passed through the gate, over the drawbridge, and they found themselves outside of the Bastille.

They threw themselves into each other's arms; there was no longer any doubt; the regent granted D'Harmental his life, and what was more, consented not to separate him from Bathilde.

This was what Bathilde and D'Harmental had never dared to hope; this life of seclusion, a punishment to many, would be to them a paradise of love, — they would be together; and what else had they desired for their future, even when they were masters of their own fate? A single sad idea crossed their minds, and both, with the sympathy of hearts who love, pronounced the name of Buvat.

At this moment the carriage stopped; at such a time everything was, for the lovers, a subject of fear. They again trembled, lest they should have given way too much to hope. The door opened, — it was the postilion.

"What do you want?" asked D'Harmental.

"I want to know where I am to take you."

"Where you are to take me! Have you no orders?"

"My orders were to take you to the Bois de Vincennes, between the Château and Nogent-sur-Marne, and here we are."

"And where is the escort?" asked D'Harmental.

"Oh, the escort left us at the barrier!"

"Oh, mon Dieu!" cried D'Harmental, while Bathilde, panting with hope, joined her hands in silence, "is it possible?"

And the chevalier jumped out of the carriage, looked round him anxiously, then clasping Bathilde in his arms, they uttered together a cry of joy and thankfulness.

They were free as the air they breathed, but the regent had ordered that they should be taken to the very place where D'Harmental had carried off Bourguignon, mistaking him for himself.

This was the only revenge of Philippe le Debonnaire.

From "THE EPITHALAMION"

By EDMUND SPENSER

OPEN the temple gates unto my love,
    Open them wide that she may enter in,
And all the posts adorn as doth behove,
And all the pillars deck with garlands trim,
For to receive this saint with honour due,
That cometh in to you.
With trembling steps, and humble reverence,
She cometh in, before the Almighty's view:
Of her, ye virgins, learn obedience,
When so ye come into these holy places,
To humble your proud faces:
Bring her up to the high altar, that she may
The sacred ceremonies there partake,
The which do endless matrimony make;
And let the roaring organ loudly play
The praises of the Lord in lively notes;
The whiles, with hollow throats,
The choristers the joyous anthem sing,
That all the woods may answer, and their echoes ring.

Behold, while she before the altar stands,
Hearing the holy priest that to her speaks,
And blesseth her with his two happy hands,
How the red roses flush up in her cheeks,
And the pure snow with goodly vermeil stain,
Like crimson dyed in grain;
That even the angels, which continually
About the sacred altar do remain,
Forget their service and about her fly,
Oft peeping in her face, that seems more fair,
The more they on it stare.

The Epithalamion

But her sad eyes, still fastened on the ground,
Are governéd with goodly modesty,
That suffers not a look to glance awry,
Which may let in a little thought unsound.
Why blush you, love, to give to me your hand,
The pledge of all our band?
Sing, ye sweet angels, Alleluia sing,
That all the woods may answer and your echo ring.

Wedding Day in Literature and Art

From "THE ONE I KNEW THE BEST OF ALL" [1]

By FRANCES HODGSON BURNETT

IT might easily have been Sister and Janey who were the principal features of the two marriages which were the first nuptial ceremonies appearing upon the stage of the Small Person's existence. But it was two of the cousins who were the brides — two of the young ladies from Grantham Hall.

Rumours of the approaching ceremonies being whispered in the school-room, the most thrilling interest was awakened. The prospect was more exciting than the breaking-up itself. There was something at once festive and imposing about it. Opinions as to the nature of the ceremony were numerous and varied. No one had ever attended a wedding, and yet somehow nearly every one could supply some detailed information.

Whispered conversation on the subject could not be wholly repressed, even by authority. From some mysterious reliable source it was ascertained that the principal features of the sacred contract were that the grown-up young lady wore a singularly resplendent and ethereal white frock, that she was wreathed with orange-blossoms and adorned with a white veil accompanied by a splendid bouquet and a grown-up gentleman. The grown-up gentleman was not dwelt upon particularly; one always asked of the bride, " Is she pretty ? " but nobody ever inquired if he was pretty. He seemed immaterial, so to speak, and when not slurred over he seemed somehow to be regarded with some slight vague distrust.

Every pupil knew what the bride was going to be dressed in, what her veil was made of, what flowers were

---

[1] *By permission of Charles Scribner's Sons, from " The One I Knew Best of All," by Frances Hodgson Burnett. Copyright, 1893, by Charles Scribner's Sons.*

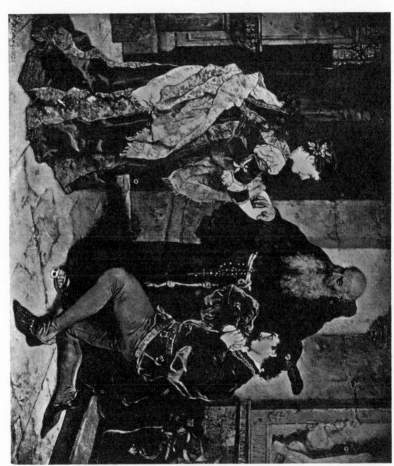

ROMEO AND JULIET.
Becker.

to compose her bouquet, but no interest whatever was felt in the possible costume of the grown-up gentleman.

The Small Person, while interested in him as a mystery, was conscious that he was regarded as a sort of necessary flaw in the occasion. The Story gave him interest to her. She had never seen him, but recollections of Ernest Maltravers, Quentin Durward, and the Master of Ravenswood gave him a nebulous form. The wedding was to be a double one, the two sisters being married at once, consequently there were two grown-up gentlemen involved, and it was rather soul-stirring to hear a vague rumour that one of them — who was very handsome, having dark eyes and a straight nose — was not smiled upon by the bride's papa, and that he had forced his way to the altar through serious parental opposition. He was not considered a sufficiently staid and well-to-do grown-up gentleman. There were suggestions of the Master of Ravenswood in this.

" I wonder if they like each other very much ? " this sentimental little Person rather timidly inquired.

But no one seemed to know anything beautiful and romantic about it, so she combined with straight nose and dark eyes the misfortunes and attributes of all the heroes in the " Secretaire," and found it thrilling that he was on the point of leading to the shrine the veil and orange-blossoms, and thus being made happy for ever after.

What a morning it was when the wedding took place. There were to be no lessons. The two young teachers were to be among the bridesmaids. They were to wear veils and wreaths themselves, and several of the most decorous little girls were going to the church to look at them. They went in a body, attired in their best frocks and feeling quite light-headed with their exalted sense of anticipation.

The sun was shining brilliantly ; everything was shining brilliantly, one felt. The cabs and omnibuses seemed to rattle by with a gay, rather reckless air, the passers-by moved more briskly than usual ; in fact, there was in the atmosphere a suggestion that everybody and everything must be going to a wedding. Everybody of course must know about it and be interested; indeed there were evidences of interest in the fact that as people passed by they nearly always glanced at the open church door, and a few rather shabby persons having loitered about the entrance, their number continued adding to itself until they formed a waiting group.

The Small Person and her companions waited also. Nobody could have thought of going into the church until the carriages had arrived and they had seen everybody get out, not to mention the fact that being inexperienced they were timid and lacked the courage to take any bold steps. They stood very much in awe of an official in a sort of gown who was known as the "Parroter," and whose function it was to show people to pews on Sunday and look pained and annoyed when little boys sneezed too frequently or dropped things.

"Perhaps the parroter would n't let us in," said some one. "Dare you ask him?"

But nobody dared do anything until the bridal party arrived. It seemed as if it never would come. The waiting in the street seemed to last hours and hours, and was filled with tumultuous agitations caused by false alarms that the carriages were coming.

"Here they are! Here they are!" somebody would cry. "I'm sure that's a carriage turning the corner down the street. Don't you see it?" And then everybody became elated and moved nervously for fear she had not a good place, and pulses quickened and hearts beat — and the carriage probably turned out to be a cab. They wandered up and down restlessly to make the time pass more quickly, and one or two bold spirits even went and peeped into the church, but retired precipitately at the approach of the "Parroter." The Small Person — after what appeared to her some sixteen hours of suspense and agitation — was pervaded by an awful secret fear that at the last moment Quentinravenswoodmaltravers had been

for ever tabooed by his bride's family and there would be
no wedding at all.

But at last, at last the bells began to ring that loud, gay,
hilarious wedding-chime, the bell-notes seeming to race
and tumble over each other in their hurry to be joyful.

There was something curiously intoxicating about it.
It was the Party over again — only more than the Party.
The Small Person looked up at the bell-tower and the blue
sky behind it. What exquisite blue sky! What soft
little fleecy white clouds! What a beautiful day! "Happy
is the bride that the sun shines on." Somebody had said
that and the sun was shining! The carriages were there
and the crowd about her was stirring with excited curiosity.
But she saw only vaporous whiteness and flowers and
dowagers' rich colours, with blots of grown-up gentlemen.
The sun was shining, the bells were chiming, the church
was filling. Happy was the bride the sun shone on. But
all brides were happy? The sun always shone on them.
What a strange, delightful, exalting event it was to be
Married!

She never knew how she was led or dragged or hustled
into the church. Some other little girl more practical and
executive than herself managed her. But presently she was
there, ensconced in a high pew in the cathedral grayness.
The church was a cathedral and impressed her deeply. She
felt religious and wondered if she ought not to say her
prayers. She was not calm enough to see detail — she
was too emotional a Small Person, and this was the first
time she had seen any one married. The vaporous whiteness, the floating veils and flowers were grouped about the
altar, the minister seemed to be taking the brides and the
grown-up gentlemen to task at some length. He called
them Dearly Beloved, but appeared to address rather
severe warnings to them. The Small Person had a vague
feeling that he was of the opinion that they would come
to a bad end if not admonished in time. She hoped they
would not — particularly Quentinravenswoodmaltravers,
whose straight nose she had been too deeply moved to

single out from the rest. For a moment or so she felt that it was so solemn to be married that it was almost conducive to low spirits. But she cheered up after the minister appeared to have relented and let them off and they moved away to the vestry. Then there was a stir among the spectators, which soon became a bustle, and she was led or dragged or hustled out into the sunshine and renewed joyous clangour of the bells.

There was a great bustle outside. The crowd of lookers-on had increased, and a policeman was keeping it back, while the carriages stood in line and closed up one by one as the floating frocks and veils, and dowagers' velvets and satins, and blots of grown-up gentlemen filled them and were driven away. The Small Person watched it all as in a dream. The bells raced and clamoured, the sun shone brighter than ever. She was only a Small Person who had really nothing to do with these splendours and who no more contemplated the magnificent prospect of being married herself than she contemplated being crowned in Westminster Abbey. Such glories as these were only for grown-up people. But they were beautiful — beautiful!

The young ladies who had been married — in full panoply of white satin and wreaths and veils — were each handed into a carriage by the grown-up gentleman they belonged to, who got into the carriage also.

After they had all driven away, the bells had ceased their clamour, and the crowd dispersed, one sharp-eyed little person made a most interesting statement.

"I saw in as their carriage drove past," she announced, "and he had Miss Grantham's head on his shoulder."

"Which one was it?" inquired the Small Person. She was *sure* it was Quentinravenswoodmaltravers.

And inquiry proved that it was.

To a Bride

"TO A BRIDE"

By NATHANIEL PARKER WILLIS

PASS thou on! for the vow is said
  That may ne'er be broken;
The trembling hand hath a blessing laid
On snowy forehead and auburn braid,
  And the word is spoken
By lips that never their word betrayed.

Pass thou on! for thy human all
  Is richly given,
And the voice that claims its holy thrall
Must be sweeter for life than music's fall,
  And, this side heaven,
Thy lips may never that trust recall.

Pass thou on! yet many an eye
  Will droop and glisten;
And the hushing heart in vain will try
To still its pulse as thy step goes by,
  And we vainly listen
For thy voice of witching melody.

Pass thou on! yet a sister's tone
  In its sweetness lingers,
Like some twin echo sent back alone,
Or the bird's soft note when its mate hath flown;
  And a sister's fingers
Will again o'er the thrilling harp be thrown.

155

And our eyes will rest on their foreheads fair,
   And our hearts awaken
Whenever we come where their voices are —
But oh, we shall think how musical were,
   Ere of thee forsaken,
The mingled voices we listened there.

Tarantella

From "TARANTELLA" [1]

By MATHILDE BLIND

" I NEED n't detain you over the number of times
we changed horses and postilions, all the bribes I
gave and the scudi I disbursed. Poor Antonella was sound
asleep in her plaid shawl and green veil, as, towards four
o'clock of the second morning of our flight, we drove
through the gates of Rome. Without further accident we
reached Raoul's studio on the Piazza Barberini, where
we had decided for the present to locate our fair charge.
She woke up with a start, and to all intents and purposes
her sleep seemed to have sufficed for a night's rest. At
any rate, no signs of lassitude impaired her complexion
or the wonderful brilliancy of her eyes, as with a kind
of childish awe she surveyed the weird surroundings of
Leroux's studio.

" Everything was new, strange and astounding, to the
Ana-Capri maiden : the numberless canvases that leant
against the lower part of the walls, the worm-eaten tapes-
tries that covered their upper portions, the yataghans, the
shields, the chain mail that hung on them, the pictures on
the easel, the casts, the masks, the anatomical *ecorches* that
filled all spaces, the hollow suit of armour that shone in
one dark corner, the skeleton with a pipe in its mouth
that filled another ; and, more horrific than all, the lay
figure which, in its silk dress and ringlets, she mistook for
the lady of the house, and which elicited a little scream
from her as she noticed its vacant stare and oddly twisted
fingers. Then there was the portrait of the cardinal that
would stare at her, move to which side she would ; the
gorgeous Persian cat that sprang loudly purring on its
master's shoulder ; the brilliant and clamorous macaw,
and the dreadful little black monkey, that, shocking to

1 From " Tarantella," published by Little, Brown, & Co.

relate, had caught her by the silk train, for which it received a caning. All this, and much more, filled her with speechless amazement.

"But before she had time to grow more accustomed to these wonders, she was hurried off by Margutta, Raoul's factotum and housekeeper, to the room that for the present was allotted to her. During her absence, ever more anxiously did Raoul and myself discuss the problem of what was to be done with her. Though demurring at first to the resolution that I had taken, he was quite willing to help me on finding me fixed in my resolution. After a few minutes he exclaimed: 'I have it! There's a priest I know, who has often sat to me, who frequents a café not far from here; many's the bottle we've emptied and the song we've sung together. He is a little rakish, I won't deny; still a priest is a priest; I'll ask him to set about this marriage business. We'll keep him in the dark about that convent escapade of your bella donna; but as long as we're fairly married according to the rules of the Church, I suppose we need have no further apprehension of pursuit or detection, as Mademoiselle Antonella had taken no vows and was therefore free to leave. However, I don't think the Signor Curato will ask many questions.'

"'By all means seek out the priest at once,' I cried; 'I am in earnest. I know I am doing what is wild and reckless; I know that this is but a simple contadina of Capri, but I love her — I love her as madly as if she were Queen of Naples. Between her and me there exist occult, magnetic affinities; for me she has got into this strait; she has entered a convent, and run away from it, and I could no more abandon her now than I could at this moment abandon the hopes of life itself, with all its prospects of gratified ambition. I don't understand the laws of this singular, unprogressive country, but I will marry her this hour, if they will permit it, and arrange all else afterwards.'

"Raoul slightly raised his eyebrows and rolled a cigarette. His cat pricked up her ears as the rustling of a silk dress was again heard along the corridor, and Antonella,

THE HONEYMOON.

De Nouy.

refreshed and resplendent, with her black, lustrous plaits newly arranged, came sweeping into the room in her long black skirt, whose dark lines brought into strong relief her embroidered chemise, her ivory shoulders, and grandly moulded arms. Raoul, assiduously placing a chair for her at the breakfast-table, which had been laid out by this time, whispered in French : ' How maddeningly those corals on the faded red handkerchief bring out her flesh tints. I already see her hung in next year's Salon with a crowd of my despairing rivals beneath her ! '

" ' Softly, softly, friend,' I answered in the same tongue; ' you will have to catch the Signor Curato first.'

" ' I will, I will ! ' cried Raoul, jumping up enthusiastically, as he gulped down the remainder of his chocolate; then smilingly kissing his hand to Antonella, he skipped out of the room.

" He returned erelong bursting with his good news; for he entered into his friends' affairs with about the same zest with which he would begin a new picture. Taking me aside, he informed me that the priest whom he had consulted was ready to marry us himself this very morning if I liked, although it would be a disciplinary offence on his part, — a consideration which he waived, on hearing he would be well rewarded for it. ' I dare say,' he went on, ' twenty-five scudi will appear ample payment to him. If your finances are exhausted I have the money all ready for you; at least you 'll be at no expense for a wedding garment or banquet.'

" When the priest arrived we accordingly received the nuptial benediction in the studio, after very scant ceremony, Raoul and his housekeeper being the witnesses."

From "THE ROMAUNT OF THE PAGE"

By ELIZABETH BARRETT BROWNING

" I SAID, ' My steed neighs in the court,
 My bark rocks on the brine,
And the warrior's vow I am under now
 To free the pilgrim's shrine;
But fetch the ring and fetch the priest
 And call that daughter of thine,
And rule she wide from my castle on Nyde
 While I am in Palestine.'

" In the dark chambere, if the bride was fair,
 Ye wis I could not see
But the steed thrice neighed, and the priest fast prayed,
 And wedd fast were we.
Her mother smiled upon her bed
As at its side we knelt to wed,
 And the bride rose from her knee
And kissed the smile of her mother dead,
 Or ever she kissed me."

The Story of the Gadsbys

From "THE STORY OF THE GADSBYS"

By RUDYARD KIPLING

SCENE. *A bachelor's bedroom — toilet-table arranged with unnatural neatness.* CAPTAIN GADSBY *asleep and snoring heavily. Time, 10.30 A. M. — a glorious autumn day at Simla. Enter delicately* CAPTAIN MAFFLIN *of Gadsby's regiment. Looks at sleeper and shakes his head, murmuring,* " *Poor Gaddy." Performs violent fantasia with hair-brushes on chair-back.*

CAPT. M. Wake up, my sleeping beauty! (*Howls :*)
   " Uprouse ye, then, my merry merry men!
    It is our opening day!
    It is our opening da-ay ! "
Gaddy, the little dicky-birds have been billing and cooing for ever and ever so long; and I 'm here!

CAPT. G. (*sitting up and yawning*). 'Mornin'. This is awf'ly good of you. ' Don't know what I should do without you. 'Pon my soul I don't. ' Have n't slept a wink all night.

CAPT. M. I did n't get in till half past eleven. ' Had a look at you then, and you seemed to be sleeping as soundly as a condemned criminal.

CAPT. G. Jack, if you want to make those disgustingly worn-out jokes, you 'd better go away. (*With portentous gravity.*) It 's the happiest day in my life.

CAPT. M. (*chuckling grimly*). Not by a very long chalk, my son. You 're going through some of the most refined torture you 've ever known. But be calm. *I* am with you. 'Shun. *Dress!*

CAPT. G. Eh! Wha-at?

CAPT. M. *Do* you suppose that you are your own master for the next twelve hours? If you *do*, of course — (*Makes for the door.*)

CAPT. G. No! For goodness' sake, old man, don't do that! You'll see me through, won't you? I've been mugging up that beastly drill, and can't remember a line of it.

CAPT. M. (*overhauling* G.'s *uniform*). Go and tub. Don't bother me. I'll give you ten minutes to dress in.

[*Interval filled by the noise as of a healthy grampus splashing the bath-room.*

CAPT. G. (*emerging from dressing-room*). What time is it?

CAPT. M. Nearly eleven.

CAPT. G. Five hours more. Oh Lord!

CAPT. M. (*aside*). 'First sign of funk, that. 'Wonder if it's going to spread. (*Aloud.*) Come along to breakfast.

CAPT. G. I can't eat anything. I don't want any breakfast.

CAPT. M. (*aside*). So early! (*Aloud.*) Captain Gadsby, I *order* you to eat breakfast, and a dashed good breakfast, too. None of your bridal airs and graces with me!

[*Leads* G. *downstairs and stands over him while he eats two chops.*

CAPT. G. (*who has looked at his watch thrice in the last* FIVE *minutes*). What time is it?

CAPT. M. Time to come for a walk. Light up.

CAPT. G. I haven't smoked for ten days, and I won't *now*. (*Takes cheroot which* M. *has cut for him and blows smoke through his nose luxuriously.*) We aren't going down the Mall, are we?

CAPT. M. (*aside*). They're all alike in these stages. (*Aloud.*) No, my vestal. We're going along the quietest road we can find.

CAPT. G. Any chance of seeing her?

CAPT. M. Innocent! No! Come along; and if you

Marriage of Convenience.

Loustaunaus.

want me for the final obsequies, don't cut my eye out with your stick.

CAPT. G. (*spinning round*). I say, is n't she the dearest creature that ever walked? What's the time? What comes after " Wilt thou take this woman " ?

CAPT. M. You go for the ring. R'clect it 'll be on the top of my right-hand little finger, and just be careful how you draw it off, because I shall have the Verger's fees somewhere in my glove.

CAPT. G. (*walking forward hastily*). D—n the Verger! Come along. It's past twelve, and I have n't seen Her since yesterday evening. (*Spinning round again.*) She's an absolute angel, Jack, and She's a dashed deal too good for me. Look here, does She come up the aisle on my arm, or how?

CAPT. M. If I thought that there was the least chance of your remembering anything for two consecutive minutes, I'd tell you. Stop passaging around like that!

CAPT. G. (*halting in the middle of the road*). I say, Jack!

CAPT. M. Keep quiet for another ten minutes, if you can, you lunatic, and walk!

[*The two tramp at five miles an hour for fifteen minutes.*

CAPT. G. What's the time? How about that cursed wedding-cake and the slippers? They don't throw 'em about in church, do they?

CAPT. M. Invariably. The Padre leads off with his boots.

CAPT. G. Confound your silly soul! Don't make fun of me. I can't stand it, and I won't.

CAPT. M. (*untroubled*). So-ooo, old horse! You 'll have to sleep for a couple of hours this afternoon.

CAPT. G. (*spinning round*). I'm *not* going to be treated like a dashed child. Understand that!

CAPT. M. (*aside*). Nerves gone to fiddle-strings. What a day we 're having! (*Tenderly putting his hand on G.'s shoulder.*) My David, how long have you known this Jonathan? Would I come up here to make a fool of you — after all these years?

Capt. G. (*penitently*). I know, I know, Jack; but I'm as upset as I can be. Don't mind what I say. Just hear me run through the drill, and see if I've got it all right: " To have and to hold for better or worse, as it was in the beginning, is now and ever shall be, world without end, so help me God. Amen."

Capt. M. (*suffocating with suppressed laughter*). Yes. That's about the gist of it. I'll prompt you if you get into a hat.

Capt. G. (*earnestly*). Yes, you'll stick by me, Jack, won't you? I'm awf'ly happy, but I don't mind telling *you* that I'm in a blue funk !

Capt. M. (*gravely*). Are you? I should never have noticed it. You don't *look* like it.

Capt. G. Don't I? That's all right. (*Spinning round.*) On my soul and honour, Jack, She's the sweetest little angel that ever came down from the sky. There isn't a woman on earth fit to speak to Her !

Capt. M. (*aside*). And this is old Gaddy! (*Aloud.*) Go on if it relieves you.

Capt. G. You can laugh ! That's all you wild asses of bachelors are fit for.

Capt. M. (*drawling*). You never would wait for the troop to come up. You aren't quite married yet, y' know.

Capt. G. Ugh! That reminds me. I don't believe I shall be able to get into my boots. Let's go home and try 'em on ! (*Hurries forward.*)

Capt. M. Wouldn't be in *your* shoes for anything that Asia has to offer.

Capt. G. (*spinning round*). That just shows your hideous blackness of soul, your dense stupidity, your brutal narrow-mindedness. There's only one fault about you. You're the best of good fellows, and I don't know what I should have done without you, but — you aren't married. (*Wags his head gravely.*) Take a wife, Jack.

Capt. M. (*with a face like a wall*). Ya-as. Whose for choice ?

Capt. G. If you're going to be a blackguard, I'm going on. What's the time?

Capt. M. (*Hums:*)

" An' since 't was very clear we drank only ginger-beer,
    Faith there must ha' been stingo in the ginger ! "

Come back, you maniac. I'm going to take you home and you're going to lie down.

Capt. G. What on earth do I want to lie down for?

Capt. M. Give me a light from your cheroot and see.

Capt. G. (*watching cheroot-butt quiver like a tuning-fork*). Sweet state I'm in!

Capt. M. You are. I'll get you a peg, and you'll go to sleep.

[*They return, and* M. *compounds a four-finger peg.*

Capt. G. O, *bus! bus!* It'll make me as drunk as an owl.

Capt. M. 'Curious thing; 't won't have the slightest effect on you. Drink it off, chuck yourself down there and go to bye-bye.

Capt. G. It's absurd. I sha'n't sleep. I *know* I sha'n't.

[*Falls into heavy doze at end of seven minutes.* Capt. M. *watches him tenderly.*

Capt. M. Poor old Gaddy ! I've seen a few turned off before, but never one who went to the gallows in this condition. 'Can't tell how it affects 'em, though. It's the thoroughbreds that sweat when they're backed into double harness. . . . And that's the man who went through the guns at Amdheran like a devil possessed of devils. (*Leans over* G.) But this is worse than the guns, old pal, — worse than the guns, isn't it? (G. *turns in his sleep and* M. *touches him clumsily on the forehead.*) Poor, dear old Gaddy ! Going like the rest of 'em — going like the rest of 'em. . . . Friend that sticketh closer than a brother . . . eight years. Dashed bit of a slip of a girl . . . eight weeks ! And — where's your friend? (*Smokes disconsolately till church clock strikes three.*)

Capt. M. Up with you and get into your kit.

Capt. G. Already? Is n't it too soon? Had n't I better have a shave?

Capt. M. *No!* You're all right. (*Aside.*) He'd chip his chin to pieces.

Capt. G. What's the hurry?

Capt. M. You've got to be there first.

Capt. G. To be stared at?

Capt. M. Exactly. You're part of the show. Where's the burnisher? Your spurs are in a shameful state.

Capt. G. (*gruffly*). Jack, I be damned if you shall do that for me.

Capt. M. (*more gruffly*). Dry up and get dressed. If I choose to clean your spurs, you're under *my* orders.

[Capt. G. *dresses.* M. *follows suit.*

Capt. M. (*critically, walking round*). M'yes, you'll do. Only don't look so like a criminal. Ring, gloves, fees — that's all right for me. Let your mustache alone. Now, if the tats are ready, we'll go.

Capt. G. (*nervously*). It's much too soon. Let's light up. Let's have a peg. Let's —

Capt. M. Let's make bally asses of ourselves.

Bells (*without*).

> Good — peo—ple — all
> To prayers — we call.

Capt. M. There go the bells! Come on — unless you'd rather not. (*They ride off.*)

Bells.   We honour the King
> And Bride's joy do bring —
> Good tidings we tell
> And ring the Dead's knell.

Capt. G. (*dismounting at the door of the church*). I say, are n't we much too soon? There are no end of people inside. I say, are n't we much too late? Stick by me, Jack! What the devil do I do?

Capt. M. Strike an attitude at the head of the aisle and wait for Her. (G. *groans as* M. *wheels him into position before three hundred eyes.*)

Capt. M. (*imploringly*). Gaddy, if you love me, for

pity's sake, for the Honour of the Regiment, stand up! Chuck yourself into your uniform! Look like a man! I 've got to speak to the Padre a minute. (G. *breaks into a gentle perspiration.*) If you wipe your face I 'll *never* be your best man again. Stand *up*. (G. *trembles visibly.*)

CAPT. M. (*returning*). She 's coming now. Look out when the music starts. There 's the organ beginning to clack.

> [*Bride steps out of 'rickshaw at church door. G. catches a glimpse of her and takes heart.*

ORGAN (*diapason and bourdon*).

> The Voice that breathed o'er Eden,
> That earliest marriage day,
> The primal marriage blessing,
> It hath not passed away.

CAPT. M. (*watching G.*). By Jove! He *is* looking well. ' Did n't think he had it in him.

CAPT. G. How long does this hymn go on for?

CAPT. M. It will be over directly. (*Anxiously.*) Beginning to bleach and gulp? Hold on, Gaddy, and think o' the Regiment.

CAPT. G. (*measuredly*). I say, there 's a big brown lizard crawling up that wall.

CAPT. M. My Sainted Mother! The last stage of collapse!

> [*Bride comes up to left of altar, lifts her eyes once to G., who is suddenly smitten mad.*

CAPT. G. (*to himself again and again*). Little Featherweight 's a woman — a woman! And I thought she was a little girl.

CAPT. M. (*in a whisper*). From the halt — inward *wheel*.

> [CAPT. G. *obeys mechanically, and the ceremony proceeds.*

PADRE . . . only unto her as long as ye both shall live?

CAPT. G. (*his throat useless*). Ha — hmmm!

CAPT. M. Say you will or you won't. There 's no second deal here.

> [*Bride gives response with perfect coolness and is given away by the father.*

CAPT. G. (*thinking to show his learning*). Jack, give me away now, *quick*.

CAPT. M. You've given yourself away quite enough. Her *right* hand, man! Repeat! repeat! "Theodore Philip." Have you forgotten your own name?

[CAPT. G. *stumbles through Affirmation which Bride repeats without a tremor.*

CAPT. M. Now the ring! Follow the Padre! Don't pull off my glove! Here it is! Great Cupid, he's found his voice!

[G. *repeats Troth in a voice to be heard to the end of the church and turns on his heel.*

CAPT. M. (*desperately*). Rein back! Back to your troop! 'T isn't half legal yet.

PADRE . . . joined together let no man put asunder.

[CAPT. G. *paralysed with fear, jibs after Blessing.*

CAPT. M. (*quickly*). On your own front, one length. Take her with you. I don't come. You've nothing to say. (CAPT. G. *jingles up to altar.*)

CAPT. M. (*in a piercing rattle meant to be a whisper*). *Kneel, you stiff-necked ruffian! Kneel!*

PADRE. . . . whose daughters ye are, so long as ye do well and are not afraid with any amazement.

CAPT. M. Dismiss! Break off! Left wheel!

[*All troop to vestry. They sign.*

CAPT. M. Kiss Her, Gaddy.

CAPT. G. (*rubbing the ink into his glove*). Eh! Wha-at?

CAPT. M. (*taking one pace to Bride*). If you don't, I shall.

CAPT. G. (*interposing an arm*). Not this journey!

[*General kissing, in which* CAPT. G. *is pursued by unknown female.*

CAPT. G. (*faintly to* M.). This is Hades! Can I wipe my face now?

CAPT. M. My responsibility has ended. Better ask *Missis* Gadsby.

[CAPT. G. *winces as if shot, and procession is Mendelssohned out of church to paternal roof, where usual tortures take place over the wedding-cake.*

The Story of the Gadsbys

CAPT. M. (*at table*). Up with you, Gaddy. They expect a speech.

CAPT. G. (*after three minutes' agony*). Ha — hmmm. (*Thunders of applause.*)

CAPT. M. Doocid good for a first attempt. Now go and change your kit while Mamma is weeping over — " the Missus." (CAPT. G. *disappears*. CAPT. M. *starts up, tearing his hair.*) It 's not *half* legal. Where are the shoes? Get an *ayah*.

AYAH. Missie Captain Sahib done gone *band karo* all the jutis.

CAPT. M. (*brandishing scabbarded sword*). Woman, produce those shoes! Some one lend me a bread-knife. We must n't crack Gaddy's head more than it is. (*Slices heel off white satin slipper and puts slippers up his sleeve.*) Where is the Bride? (*To the company at large.*) Be tender with that rice. It 's a heathen custom. Give me the big bag.

    [*Bride slips out quietly into 'rickshaw and departs towards the sunset.*

CAPT. M. (*in the open*). Stole away, by Jove. So much the worse for Gaddy! Here he is. Now, Gaddy, this 'll be livelier than Amdheran! Where 's your horse?

CAPT. G. (*furiously, seeing that the women are out of earshot.*) Where the — is my *wife?*

CAPT. M. Half-way to Mahasu by this time. You 'll have to ride like young Lochinvar.

    [*Horse comes round on his hind legs ; refuses to let* G. *handle him.*

CAPT. G. Oh, you will, will you? Get round, you brute — you hog — you beast ! Get *round.*

    [*Wrenches horse's head over, nearly breaking lower jaw ; swings himself into saddle, and sends home both spurs in the midst of a sputtering gale of Best Patna.*

CAPT. M. For your life and your love — ride, Gaddy ! — And God bless you!

    [*Throws half a pound of rice at* G., *who disappears, bowed forward on the saddle, in a cloud of sunlit dust.*

CAPT. M. I 've lost old Gaddy. (*Lights cigarette and strolls off, singing absently :*)

" You may carve it on his tombstone, you may cut it on
    his card,
  That a young man married is a young man marred ! "

MISS DEERCOURT (*from her horse*). Really, Captain Mafflin, you are more plain-spoken than polite !

CAPT. M. (*aside*). They say marriage is like cholera. 'Wonder who 'll be the next victim.

> [*White satin slipper slides from his sleeve and falls at
> his feet. Left wondering.*

"CYNTHIA'S BRIDAL EVENING"

By JOHN KEATS

THE evening weather was so bright and clear,
   That men of health were of unusual cheer;
Stepping like Homer at the trumpet's call,
Or young Apollo on the pedestal:
And lovely women were as fair and warm,
As Venus looking sideways in alarm.
The breezes were ethereal and pure,
And crept through half-closed lattices to cure
The languid sick; it cooled their fevered sleep,
And soothed them into slumbers full and deep.
Soon they awoke clear-eyed: nor burned with thirsting,
Nor with hot fingers, nor with temples bursting:
And springing up, they met the wondering sight
Of their dear friends, nigh foolish with delight;
Who feel their arms and breasts, and kiss, and stare,
And on their placid foreheads part the hair.
Young men and maidens at each other gazed,
With hands held back, and motionless, amazed
To see the brightness in each other's eyes;
And so they stood filled with a sweet surprise,
Until their tongues were loosed in poesy.
Therefore no lover did of anguish die:
But the soft numbers, in that moment spoken,
Made silken ties that never may be broken.

Wedding Day in Literature and Art

From "PEOPLE WE PASS"[1]

By JULIAN RALPH

THE bride, a tiny, pert little blond German, with eyes that shone with mischievous expression, was surrounded by the other girls. To their surprise she would not take off her hat and cloak, she would not sit down, she would not say why. She would only laugh silently with her tiny beadlike eyes. It was evident that between excitement and self-consciousness she was undergoing an intense strain. Presently there came a stalwart young fellow, blond also and a German, who, from a physical standpoint, was certainly handsome. And he was more than commonly intelligent-looking as well. His dress, under the circumstances, was very peculiar. He wore a cardigan jacket, and shabby trousers tucked in cowhide boots, to which were affixed the heavy spurred irons with which telegraph-line repairers climb the poles on which the wires are strung. In one hand he swung a cap and a stout new hempen rope. The young men gathered around him and loudly voiced their astonishment, for this, it appeared, was the bridegroom. They asked him if he had just quit work, and how long it would take him to dress, and " what it all meant, anyhow."

" Is the kag of beer here ? " he asked the jolly widow in German. She replied with an affirmative series of chuckles and indications of pent-up merriment, and a great bustle ensued. As a result there was brought into the room a table spread with cold meats, German cheeses, pickles, strange cakes with the fruits outside, and other cakes covered with icing and rubbed with red sugar. Then followed the inevitable beer — mainstay and chief delight of the masses — in a keg on a wooden horse, and

---

1 *From " People We Pass," published by Harper & Brothers.*

THE WEDDING DRESS.
Worms.

accompanied by more than a score of heavy beer-saloon glasses with handles. This was the bridegroom's answer to the questions of his friends, and, being practical in its way, was received with better grace than the girls had accorded to the bride's responses in mysterious and mischievous glances.

The next important personage to arrive was the clergyman, a shrivelled little German, in a battered beaver hat and suit of black, illuminated by one of those high white collars that show no break, but seem to have been made and laundered on the necks of those who wear them. He rubbed his hands before the stove, and after consuming a palmful of snuff, put to violent use a handkerchief of so pronounced a red that it made him seem to suffer from an extraordinary hemorrhage of the nose. When he was, as it seemed to the others, very good and ready, he took from a tail pocket of his coat something very like a woman's striped stocking, and fitted its open end over his skull. Then the stocking took the guise of a liberty cap. During all this time he spoke to no one, but carried the air of a man of business bent upon a perfunctory performance, and determined to execute it properly and with despatch. His stocking adjusted, he might have spoken, — indeed, he cleared his throat as if to do so, — but the arrival of the tardiest of the guests prevented his doing so. This new arrival was, next to the bride and groom, the person of most distinction in the company, Mr. Barney Kelly, the reporter.

" Ah, there, Barney ! " all the men called out.

" Ah, there ! put it there," said the genial journalist, making a pantomimic offer of a shake of his hand to all at once.

. . . .

" Vell," said the parson, facing the company, " do ve been all retty ? "

" Min," said the bridegroom, turning to the bride, " have you told any one ? "

" Well, I just guess not," said the bride.

" Very well, then," said the bridegroom. "Gents and ladies all. The first time I seen Minnie Bechman I was at work on a pole just in front of this window, where she was sitting, once, on a visit to these old friends of her. She took to me, and — you know how it is yourselves — and we agreed to get married. Well, then, the thing was how we was to get married so as to make a sensation in the city. Well, then, Barney Kelly here, he put the scheme into my head that we was to get married on a po —"

" Hully gee, Chris!" exclaimed the great journalist, "don't give the snap away so quick."

" Go on, Chris!" " Go on, Dutch!" cried the others.

" No; you go 'head and tell it, Barney," said the bridegroom. "Tell it just the way you'll write it up."

" I've written it up a'ready," said the journalist. "It's a corker, boys — ladies and gentlemen — a corker; a hull collum in the *Camera!*"

" Say, fellers, that's great, hain't it?" one visitor exclaimed. "Is our names dere in de *Camera*, Barney?"

" Every son of a gun's name that got invited is in there, you kin bet," said Mr. Kelly. "Now, I'll give you the whole snap. You see this is the age of sensations, and nothing but sensations goes. Understand? . . . People have got married in Trinity steeple, in a row-boat on the river, in a cab in Central Park, in a balloon, on skates, by telephone and telegraph, and on horseback — in fact, more ways than you can shake a stick at — but Dutch an' me agreed we never heard of no one gittin' married on a telegraph pole. He's a line-man an' climbing them sticks is his business, ladies; so the only thing was whether Minnie wouldn't be a-scared — see? Her mother wouldn't have it; but there wasn't no poles around her house, anyhow; and besides, Dutch wanted the pole where he was when he first seen Minnie. He told her all about it an' she was dead game, and she says, ' We might as well be romantic wunst in our life' — see?"

" So," said the bridegroom, vastly impatient to play his

part, "we did n't tell Min's mother she was a-goin' to get married at all; and as for Minnie being a-scared, why, here goes for the first wedding alongside the wires."

. . . .

The bridegroom, a picture of impatience, held out one powerful arm, crooked at the elbow, and the diminutive bride leaped into it and was carried as lightly out of the room as if she weighed no more than a shawl. All the young men and many of the girls trooped downstairs behind the happy man and his freight, the clanking of the irons on his boots drowning the noises of all their feet. The clergyman went to one of the front windows, and throwing it open, leaned out, book in hand; all who remained in the room crowded behind him and at the other window. Within a few feet — say twice an easy-reaching distance — rose the great mast-like pole, and even with the next floor above were the cross-bars on which the wires were fastened. Five minutes before, not many persons had been seen on the street, but now the sidewalk was thronged, and men, women, and children, some shouting, some laughing, and some calling loudly to others at a distance, were hurrying to the scene. Perceptible above the other sounds was the thud, thud, thud, of the lineman's spikes or "irons," as he drove them into the pole. He mounted steadily upward, circling the pole with one arm, while his bride rested partly on the other and partly on a hempen rope which was arranged so as to form a loop under her body and over his farther shoulder.

"Don't spill me, Chris," she said in a tone betraying at least a little nervousness.

"Don't — wiggle — an' — I — won't," said he, punctuating each word with a thud and a step upward.

At first the villageful of people who lived on that one block had been aroused by the rumour that a girl was climbing a telegraph pole, but the spectacle of the man and the girl working their way towards the heights that thousands inhabit, but reach exclusively by stairs or elevators, gave rise to the report that the man was a maniac. The invention grew more ingenious as it flew, until it got about that the maniac was going to hang himself and the girl from the cross-bars. In a minute and a half the block, from stoop-line to stoop-line, was crowded. If any policeman was in the neighbourhood, he did not interfere.

" Ready ! be quick about it ! " said the bridegroom ; and at the words the little German parson, leaning so far out of the window that the end of his stocking-like cap fell in front of his nose, began to read the marriage service, in German, at breakneck speed. In the wild flight of words there were perceptible haltings, marked with a " Yah " by one or the other of the couple on the pole. Before it seemed possible the ceremony could have reached its conclusion, the minister stopped, slapped his book shut, and said, in what he intended for the Queen's English, " I now bronounce you man und vife. May Gott in heffun pless you bote ! "

A roar of applause marked their successful descent to the street, and presently the bride and groom, the former glowing from excitement, and the latter nursing his arm with rude pantomime, reappeared in the room, preceded by some and followed by the others of those who had gone down to the street with them. Then there was great excitement. The young men seized the proud and grinning bridegroom's hands and jerked him violently about the room in the excess of their admiration. The young women crowded the bride into a corner and intended to give vent to their surprise and delight, but their excitement greatly exaggerated their natural lack of conversational gifts. When they did recover their powers of speech, the results were not such as one is accustomed to in feminine gatherings in the heart of the town. . . .

" It was great, Minnie."

" It was out of sight."

" For Gord's sakes ! I don't see how you could ever do it."

" I did n't care ! " This by the bride.

" She hit me for a silk dress for doing it, just the same," said her husband.

" Is tha-a-t so, Minnie ! Did yer get a silk dress? "

" I did so, Ma-a-a-ggie."

" My Gord, girls ! ain't Chris good to her ? "

" Well," said Ma-a-a-ggie, " I 'd marry anny man for a silk dress."

"And who would n't, I 'd like to know?" asked little Elsa Muller, the youngest girl in the room.

From "CROWNED AND WEDDED"[1]

By ELIZABETH BARRETT BROWNING

THE minster was alight that day, but not with fire, I
ween,
And long-drawn glitterings swept adown that mighty aisled
scene.
The priests stood stoled in their pomp, the sworded chiefs
in theirs,
And so, the collared knights, and so, the civil ministers,
And so the waiting lords and dames — and little pages best
At holding trains — and legates so, from countries east
and west.
So, alien princes, native peers, and high-born ladies bright,
Along whose brows, the Queen's, new crowned, flashed
coronets to light.
And so, the people at the gates, with priestly hands on high,
Which bring the first anointing to all legal majesty.
And so the dead — who lie in rows beneath the minster
floor,
There, verily an awful state maintaining evermore;
The statesman whose clean palm will kiss no bribe whate'er
it be.
The courtier who, for no fair queen, will rise up to his
knee.
The court-dame who, for no court-tire, will leave her
shroud behind.
The laureate who no courtlier rhyme than "dust to dust"
can find.
The kings and queens who having made that vow and worn
that crown,
Descend unto lower thrones and darker, deep adown!

[1] *Written upon the marriage of Queen Victoria.*

Crowned and Wedded

Dieu et mon droit — what is 't to them ? — what meaning
    can it have ? —
The King of kings, the right of death — God's judgment
    and the grave.
And when betwixt the quick and dead, the young, fair queen
    had vowed,
The living shouted " May she live ! Victoria, live ! " aloud.
And as the loyal shouts went up, true spirits prayed between,
" The blessings happy monarchs have, be thine, O crowned
    queen ! "
But now before her people's face she bendeth hers anew,
And calls them, while she vows, to be her witness thereunto,
She vowed to rule, and in that oath her childhood put away.
She doth maintain her womanhood, in vowing love to-day.
O, lovely lady ! — let her vow — such lips become such
    vows,
And fairer goeth bridal wreath than crown with vernal
    brows.
O, lovely lady ! — let her vow ! — yea, let her vow to
    love ! —
And though she be no less a queen — with purples hung
    above
The pageant of a court behind, the royal kin around,
And woven gold to catch her looks turned maidenly to
    ground,
Yet may the bride-veil hide from her a little of that state,
While loving hopes, for retinues, about her sweetness wait.
She vows to love who vowed to rule — (the chosen at her
    side)
Let none say, God preserve the queen ! — but rather, Bless
    the bride !
None blow the trump, none bend the knee, none violate
    the dream
Wherein no monarch but a wife, she to herself may seem.
Or if ye say, Preserve the queen ! — oh, breathe it inward
    low —
She is a *woman*, and *beloved!* — and 't is enough but so.

179

From "ST. PATRICK'S EVE"

By CHARLES LEVER

IT was a fine day in spring — the mountain and the lake were bright in the sunshine — the valley, rich in the promise of the coming year, was already green with the young wheat — the pleasant sounds of happy labour rose from the fields fresh-turned by the plough — the blue smoke curled into thin air from many a cabin, no longer mean-looking and miserable as before, but with signs of comfort around, in the trim hedge of the little garden and the white walls that glistened in the sun.

Towards the great mountain above the lake, however, many an eye was turned from afar, and many a peasant lingered to gaze upon the scene which now marked its rugged face.

Along the winding path which traced its zigzag course from the lake-side to the little glen where Owen's cabin stood, a vast procession could be seen moving on foot and horseback. Some, in country cars, assisted up the steep by strong men's shoulders ; others, mounted in twos and threes upon some slow-footed beast; but the great number walking, or, rather, clambering their way — for in their eagerness to get forward, they, each moment, deserted the path to breast the ferny mountain-side. The scarlet cloaks of the women, as they fluttered in the wind, and their white caps, gave a brilliancy to the picture, which, as the masses emerged from the depths of some little dell and disappeared again, had all the semblance of some gorgeous panorama. Nor was the eye the only sense gladdened by the spectacle — for even in the valley could be heard the clear ringing laughter as they went along, and the wild cheer of merriment that ever and anon burst forth from happy hearts, while, high above all, the pleasant sounds of the bagpipe rose, as seated upon an ass and entrusted to the guidance of a boy, the musician moved along; his inspiriting strains taken advantage of at every spot of level ground by some merry souls, who would not "lose so much good music."

As the head of the dense column wound its way upward, one little group could be seen by those below, and were saluted by many a cheer and the waving of handkerchiefs. These were a party, whose horses and gear seemed far better than the rest; and among them rode a gentleman mounted on a strong pony,—his chief care was bestowed less on his own beast than in guiding that of a young country girl who rode beside him. She was enveloped in a long blue cloak of dark cloth, beneath which she wore a white dress; a white ribbon floated through her hair, too; but in her features and the happy smile upon her lip, the bride was written more palpably than in all these.

High above her head, upon a pinnacle of rock, a man stood, gazing at the scene; at his side a little child of some four or five years, whose frantic glee seemed perilous in such a place, while his wild accents drew many an upward glance from those below, as he cried,—

"See, Nony, see! Mary is coming to us at last!"

This, too, was a "St. Patrick's Eve," and a happy one. May Ireland see many such!

"WEDDING WORDS"

By W. C. BENNETT

A JEWEL for my lady's ear,
　A jewel for her finger fine,
A diamond for her bosom dear,
　Her bosom that is mine.

Dear glances for my lady's eyes,
　Dear looks around her form to twine,
Dear kisses for the lips I prize,
　Her dear lips that are mine.

Dear breathings to her, soft and low,
　Of how my lot she's made divine,
Dear silences my love that show
　For her whose love is mine.

Dear cares no cloud shall shade her way,
　That gladness only on her shine,
That she be happy as the May
　Whose lot is one with mine.

Dear wishes hovering round her life
　And tending thoughts, and dreams divine,
To feed with perfect joy the wife
　Whose happiness is mine.

Paul Gosslet's Confessions

From "PAUL GOSSLET'S CONFESSIONS"

By CHARLES LEVER

GREAT news has the post brought. Sir Morris Stamer is going out Lord High Commissioner to the Ionian Islands, and offers to take me as private sec.

It is a brilliant position, and one to marry on. I shall ask Lizzy to-day.

Wednesday, all settled; — but what have I not gone through these last three days! She loves me to distraction; but she'll tell nothing, — nothing till we're married. She says, and with truth, "confidence is the nurse of love." I wish she was n't so coy. I have not even kissed her hand. She says Irish girls are all coy.

We are to run away, and be married at a place called Articlane. I don't know why we run away; but this is another secret I'm to hear later on. Quiet and demure as she looks, Lizzy has a very decided disposition.

. . . .

I was sound asleep, though the noise of the storm was actually deafening, when Lizzy again tapped at my door, and at last opening it slightly, pushed a lighted candle inside, and disappeared. If there be a dreary thing in life, it is to get up before day of a dark, raw morning, in a room destitute of all comfort and convenience, and proceed to wash and dress in cold, gloom, and misery, with the consciousness that what you are about to do not only might be safer and better undone, but may, and not at all improbably will, turn out the rashest act of your life.

Over and over I said to myself, "If I were to tell her that I have a foreboding, — a distinct foreboding of calamity; — that I dreamed a dream, and saw myself on a raft, while waves, mountain high, rose above me, and depths yawned beneath, — dark, fathomless, and terrible, — would she mind it? I declare, on my sacred word of honour, I declare I think she'd laugh at me!"

"Are you ready?" whispered a soft voice at the door; and I saw at once my doom was pronounced.

Noiselessly, stealthily, we crept down the stairs, and, crossing the little flagged kitchen, undid the heavy bars of the door. Shall I own that a thought of treason shot through me as I stood with the great bolt in my hands, and the idea flashed across me, "What if I were to let it fall with a crash, and awake the household?" Did she divine what was passing in my head, as she silently took the bar from me, and put it away?

We were now in the open air, breasting a swooping nor'wester that chilled the very marrow of my bones. She led the way through the dark night as though it were noonday, and I followed, tumbling over stones and rocks and tufts of heather, and falling into holes, and scrambling out again like one drunk. I could hear her laughing at me too,— she who so seldom laughed; and it was with difficulty she could muster gravity enough to say she hoped I had not hurt myself.

We gained the pier at last, and, guided by a lantern held by one of the boatmen, we saw the boat bobbing and tossing some five feet down below. Lizzy sprang in at once, amidst the applauding cheers of the crew, and then several voices cried out, "Now, sir! Now, your honour!" while two stout fellows pushed me vigorously, as though to throw me into the sea. I struggled and fought manfully, but in vain. I was jerked off my legs, and hurled headlong down, and found myself caught below by some strong arms, though not until I had half sprained my wrist, and barked one of my shins from knee to instep. These sufferings soon gave way to others, as I became seasick, and lay at the bottom of the boat, praying we might all go down, and end a misery I could no longer endure. That spars struck me, and ballast rolled over me; that heavy-footed sailors trampled me, and seemed to dance on me, were things I minded not. Great waves broke over the bows, and came in sheets of foam and water over me. What cared I? I had that deathlike sickness that makes all life hideous, and I felt I had reached a depth of degradation and misery in which there was only one desire, — that for death. That we succeeded in clearing the point which formed one side of the bay was little short of a miracle, and I remember the cheer the boatmen gave as the danger was passed, and my last hope of our all going down left me. After this, I know no more.

A wild confusion of voices, a sort of scuffling uproar, a grating sound, and more feet dancing over me, aroused me. I looked up. It was dawn; a gray murky streak lay towards the horizon, and sheets of rain were carried swiftly on the winds. We were being dragged up on a low shingly shore, and the men — up to their waist in water — were carrying the boat along.

As I looked over the gunwale, I saw a huge strong fellow rush down the slope, and breasting the waves as they beat, approach the boat. Lizzy sprang into his arms at once, and he carried her back to land triumphantly. I suppose at any other moment a pang of jealousy might have shot through me. Much seasickness, like perfect love, overcometh all things. I felt no more, as I gazed, than if it had been a bundle he had been clasping to his bosom.

They lifted me up, and laid me on the shingle.

" Oh, do, Tom ; he is such a good creature ! " said a voice which, low as it was, I heard distinctly.

" By all that's droll ! this is the Cockney I met at Morrison's ! " cried a loud voice. I looked up; and there, bending over me, was Counsellor MacNamara, the bland stranger I had fallen in with at Dublin.

" Are you able to get on your legs," asked he, " or shall we have you carried ? "

" No," said I, faintly ; " I'd rather lie here."

" Oh, we can't leave him here, Tom ; it's too cruel."

" I tell you, Lizzy," said he, impatiently, " there's not a minute to lose."

" Let them carry him, then," said she, pleadingly.

I mildly protested my wish to live and die where I lay ; but they carried me up somewhere, and they put me to bed, and they gave me hot drinks, and I fell into, not a sleep, but a trance, that lasted twenty-odd hours.

" Faix ! they had a narrow escape of it," were the first intelligible words I heard on awaking. " They were only just married and druv off when old Dan Dudgeon came up, driving like mad. He was foaming with passion, and said if he went to the gallows for it, he 'd shoot the rascal that abused his hospitality and stole his daughter. The lady left this note for honour."

It went thus : —

DEAR MR. GOSSLETT, — You will, I well know, bear me no ill-will for the little fraud I have practised on you. It was an old engagement, broken off by a momentary imprudence on Tom's part ; but as I knew he loved me, it was forgiven. My father would not have ever consented to the match, and we were driven to this strait. I entreat you to forgive and believe me

Most truly yours,

LIZZY MACNAMARA.

"ELIPHALET CHAPIN'S WEDDING" [1]

By WILL CARLETON

'TWAS when the leaves of autumn were by tempest-
fingers picked,
Eliphalet Chapin started to become a benedict;
With an ancient two-ox waggon to bring back his new-found
goods,
He hawed and gee'd and floundered through some twenty
miles o' woods;
With prematrimonial ardour he his horned steeds did press,
But Eliphalet's wedding journey did n't bristle with success.
      Oh no, woe, woe!
      With candour to digress,
Eliphalet's wedding journey did n't tremble with success.

He had not carried five miles his mouth-disputed face,
When his wedding garments parted in some inconvenient
place;
He'd have given both his oxen to a wife that now was
dead,
For her company two minutes with a needle and a thread.
But he pinned them up, with twinges of occasional distress,
Feeling that his wedding would n't be a carnival of dress:
      " Haw, Buck! "
      Gee, Bright!
      Derned pretty mess."
No; Eliphalet was not strictly a spectacular success.

He had not gone a ten mile when a wheel demurely broke,
A disunited family of felloe, hub, and spoke;
It joined, with flattering prospects, the Society of Wrecks;
And he had to cut a sapling, and insert it 'neath the " ex."

---

[1] *From " Farm Festivals," published by Harper & Brothers.*

187

So he ploughed the hills and valleys with that Doric wheel
    and tire,
Feeling that his wedding journey was not all he could
    desire.
        " Gee, Bright !
        G'long, Buck ! "
        He shouted, hoarse with ire :
No ; Eliphalet's wedding journey none in candour could
    admire !

He had not gone fifteen miles with extended face forlorn,
When night lay down upon him hard, and kept him there
    till morn ;
And when the daylight chuckled at the gloom within his
    mind,
One ox was " Strayed or Stolen," and the other hard to find.
So yoking Buck as usual, he assumed the part of Bright
(Constituting a menagerie diverting to the sight);
        With " Haw, Buck !
        Gee, Buck !
        Sha' n't get there till night."
No ; Eliphalet's wedding journey was not one intense delight.

Now, when he drove his equipage up to his sweetheart's
    door,
The wedding guests had tired and gone just half an hour
    before ;
The preacher had from sickness an unprofitable call,
And had sent a voice proclaiming that he could n't come
    at all ;
The parents had been prejudiced by some one, more or
    less,
And the sire the bridegroom greeted with a different word
    from " bless."
        " Blank your head,
        You Blank ! " he said ;
        " We 'll break this off, I guess ! "
No ; Eliphalet's wedding was not an unqualified success.

Eliphalet Chapin's Wedding

Now, when the bride saw him arrive, she shook her crimson
    locks,
And vowed to goodness gracious she would never wed an
    ox;
And with a vim deserving rather better social luck,
She eloped that day by daylight with a swarthy Indian
    " buck,"
With the presents in the pockets of her woollen wedding-
    dress;
And " Things ain't mostly with me," quoth Eliphalet, " I
    confess."
            No — no;
            As things go,
            No fair mind 't would impress
That Eliphalet Chapin's wedding was an unalloyed success.

From "LORNA DOONE"

By R. D. BLACKMORE

HOWEVER humble I might be, no one knowing any-thing of our part of the country would for a moment doubt that now here was a great to-do and talk of John Ridd and his wedding. The fierce fight with the Doones so lately, and my leading of the combat (though I fought not more than need be), and the vanishing of Sir Counsellor, and the galloping madness of Carver, and the religious fear of the women that this last was gone to hell — for he him-self had declared that his aim, while he cut through the yeomanry — also their remorse that he should have been made to go thither, with all his children left behind — these things, I say (if ever I can again contrive to say anything), had led to the broadest excitement about my wedding of Lorna. We heard that people meant to come from more than thirty miles around, upon excuse of seeing my stature and Lorna's beauty; but, in good truth, out of sheer curiosity and the love of meddling.

Our clerk had given notice that not a man should come inside the door of his church without shilling fee, and women (as sure to see twice as much) must every one pay two shillings. I thought this wrong; and, as church-warden, begged that the money might be paid into mine own hands when taken. But the clerk said that was against all law; and he had orders from the parson to pay it to him without any delay. So, as I always obey the parson when I care not much about a thing, I let them have it their own way, though feeling inclined to believe sometimes that I ought to have some of the money.

Dear mother arranged all the ins and outs of the way in which it was to be done; and Annie and Lizzie, and all

THE HONEYMOON.
Tondouze.

the Snowes, and even Ruth Huckaback (who was there, after great persuasion), made such a sweeping of dresses that I scarcely knew where to place my feet, and longed for a staff to put by their gowns. Then Lorna came out of a pew half-way, in a manner which quite astonished me, and took my left hand in her right, and I prayed God that it were done with.

My darling looked so glorious that I was afraid of glancing at her, yet took in all her beauty. She was in a fright, no doubt, but nobody should see it; whereas I said (to myself, at least), "I will go through it like a grave-digger."

Lorna's dress was of pure white, clouded with faint lavender (for the sake of the old Earl Brandir), and as simple as need be, except for perfect loveliness. I was afraid to look at her, as I said before, except when each of us said, "I will;" and then each dwelt upon the other.

It is impossible for any who have not loved as I have to conceive my joy and pride when, after ring and all was done, and the parson had blessed us, Lorna turned to look at me with her glances of subtle fun subdued by this great act.

Her eyes, which none on earth may ever equal or compare with, told me such a depth of comfort, yet awaiting further commune, that I was almost amazed, thoroughly as I knew them. Darling eyes, the sweetest eyes, the loveliest, the most loving eyes — the sound of a shot rang through the church, and those eyes were filled with death.

Lorna fell across my knees when I was going to kiss her, as the bridegroom is allowed to do, and encouraged, if he needs it: a flood of blood came out upon the yellow wood of the altar steps; and at my feet lay Lorna, trying to tell me some last message out of her faithful eyes. I lifted her up, and petted her, and coaxed her, but it was no good; the only sign of life remaining was a spurt of bright red blood.

   •   •   •   •   •   •   •   •   •

I was surprised to see Ruth excited, her character being so calm and quiet. And I tried to soothe her with my feeble hand, as now she knelt before me.

" Dear cousin, the doctor must know best. Annie says so every day. Else what has he been brought up for ? "

" Brought up for slaying and murdering. Twenty doctors killed King Charles, in spite of all the women. Will you leave it to me, John ? I have a little will of my own, and I am not afraid of doctors. Will you leave it to me, dear John ? I have saved your Lorna's life. And now I will save yours; which is a far, far easier business."

" You have saved my Lorna's life ? What do you mean by talking so ? "

" Only what I say, Cousin John. Though perhaps I overprize my work. But at any rate she says so."

" I do not understand," was all I could say for a very long time.

" Will you understand, if I show you Lorna ? I have feared to do it, for the sake of you both. But now Lorna is well enough, if you think that you are, Cousin John. Surely you will understand, when you see your wife."

Following her to the very utmost of my mind and heart, I felt that all she said was truth, and yet I could not make it out.

Before I had time to listen much for the approach of footsteps, Ruth came back, and behind her Lorna, coy as if of her bridegroom, and hanging back with her beauty. Ruth banged the door and ran away, and Lorna stood before me.

Neighbour Jackwood

From "NEIGHBOUR JACKWOOD"[1]

By J. T. TROWBRIDGE

THERE was to be a wedding in the village to which
the Dunburys were invited; and it devolved upon
Hector to represent the family. To his mother's surprise
and gratification he engaged to undertake the responsibility
upon one condition. "Charlotte," said he, "shall go
with me."

Charlotte shrank from the thought of seeing society;
but she had no good excuse to offer — not even on the
score of dress; for since her residence with the Dunburys
she had been liberally provided for in that respect. Notwithstanding, therefore, certain forebodings she had, she
consented to accompany Hector.

The ceremony was to take place in the evening; and in
due season Corny brought the horse and buggy to the door.

" It is a brave wedding we are going to," said Hector, as
they drove away. " The fair young bride is in her thirty-
fifth summer, — a little gray and faded but for the virtues
of a judicious hair-wash and the excellent care taken of
her complexion. When I was a school-boy, aged ten, she
was the belle of the village, and had as many lovers as she
could count on her fingers and toes. Old men renewed
their youth to become her suitors, and boys were as sure to
fall in love with her as they were to have down on their
chins. I was one of the predestinated, and at sixteen experienced two days of excessive melancholy in consequence
of a rejection. Well, having suffered the first and second
generation of her admirers to pass away, she has chosen
one out of a third thin brood of weaklings, who have man-

---

[1] *By permission of Lee & Shepard, from " Neighbour Jackwood," by J. T.
Trowbridge.*

13   193

aged to get up a feeble show of the ancient custom in these latter days."

Charlotte hoped the bridegroom was worthy.

"Oh, he is worthy enough; although, to speak truth, she would not have lowered even her haughty glance to his level five years ago."

"Why will she now, then?"

"Because he stands to her in the interesting position of a last chance for a husband. And it is so very horrible to live an old maid, you know."

"But," said Charlotte, "it is dreadful — such a union."

"Oh, it will do, it will do, as matches average."

Arrived at the bride's house, Hector and Charlotte were ushered into the presence of a large company, some silent, some conversing in subdued voices, and all very solemn.

"If I had never been to a wedding before," whispered Hector, "I should think we had made a mistake, and got into a funeral."

Suddenly there was a hush, and the happy pair, appearing with the bridesmaids and groomsmen, marched to the place assigned them in the light of wax candles. The centre of observation, of course, was the bride. She was of such commanding presence that the pretty Mr. Creston, with his weak face and slender shoulders, seemed scarcely noticeable at her side.

"How pale she looks," said Bertha Wing, who sat with Mr. Rukely at Charlotte's left hand. "What a strange brightness in her eye!"

Hector turned with a smile which sent the blood tingling to her cheeks.

"She is taking her last look at her bright ideal, Bertha. Or perhaps the phantoms of old-time lovers are flitting between her and the light."

Bertha, troubled: "She will be happier when it is all over."

Hector: "So you may say of a drowning man."

Mr. Rukely: "Let us have charity."

Neighbour Jackwood

The ceremony was performed by a staid old clergyman of the village, who married the happy couple fast and strong, and blessed the union. Congratulations and kisses followed; and at length refreshments were introduced, — jellies, nuts, coffee, and several kinds of costly cake, all very fine and very indigestible, together with a feast of reason, to which the company was invited by the bridegroom's uncle. This was 'Squire Greenwich, a village justice, — a wrinkle-browed, snuff-taking, old-fashioned individual, with a wise grimace, spectacles, and stiff iron gray hair stuck up all over his head.

"My daughter Etty," said he, enunciating with slow precision, "has prepared a poetical address, appropriate to the occasion, which she will proceed to deliver. Etty!"

A girl of thirteen, with a large forehead and great eyes, supposed to be a genius, stepped forward promptly.

"It's all her own composition," remarked the child's mother by way of prologue. "She wrote it without any assistance."

"Mrs. Greenwich," interrupted her husband, with lofty disapprobation, "I am talking now! Daughter!" raising his hand, "one, two, three, — begin!"

At the word, Etty rattled away, like a militia company firing at command, with a volley of blank verses levelled at the newly married pair.

Mother parenthetically: "Not quite so fast, daughter."

Father severely: "I'll dictate, if you please, Mrs. Greenwich!"

The lady nodded deferentially, Etty went on, holding her hands stiffly folded across her lap, and looking down, as if reciting to the carpet. The substance of the poem was, that the happy pair were a strong oak and a graceful vine yoked together in the car of matrimony, and sailing over a sapphire ocean, in a little Eden of their own, full of flowery fountains, rainbows, the prodigal son, and the wise virgins with oil in their lamps. Quite a round of applause greeted the conclusion.

"I want you all to understand," said the mother of the

195

genius, "that the poem was composed in one hour and forty minutes — "

"Mrs. Greenwich, I was about to speak ! "

Mrs. G. meekly : "Oh, certainly ! "

Mr. G. : "Daughter ! "

Young genius prettily : "What, father ? "

"I want you to recite the last part again, commencing at the line, 'There Flora spreads,' and let your voice rise at 'spangled groves.' Slowly and distinctly."

Encouraged by the praises already bestowed, Etty repeated the concluding lines with improved confidence, and won additional applause. The bride, who had borne up under the infliction with smiling patience, thanked the little prodigy for her compliments and good wishes, and asked for a copy of the verses.

"A copy for me, too, Etty," said the bridegroom.

Blushing bridesmaid : "I speak for a copy ! "

Two or three, in a breath : "Me, too, Etty ! "

Chorus of voices : "Wonderful genius ! " — "Be-e-e-e-eau-tiful ! " — "Sweet pretty ! " — "Ought to be printed ! "

'Squire Greenwich : "Daughter, what have you got to say ? "

Young genius ready with a speech : "I thank you all very kindly for your good opinion — "

Mrs. Greenwich, in a whisper : "Go on, — what is it about talents ? "

"If God has seen fit to endow me with talents, I ought not to take any credit to myself, but show my gratitude by trying to make good use of them. At the same time I trust my friends will be less ready to praise than to tell me of my faults."

More applause. Little prodigy's head quite turned. Mrs. G. excited and silly. Mr. G. prosy on the subject of his daughter's talents.

"TO MY DAUGHTER,

ON BEING SEPARATED FROM HER ON HER MARRIAGE"

BY MRS. HUNTER

DEAR to my heart as life's warm stream
    Which animates this mortal clay,
For thee I court the waking dream,
    And deck with smiles the future day ;
And thus beguile the present pain
With hopes that we shall meet again.

Yet, will it be as when the past
    Twined every joy, and care, and thought,
And o'er our minds one mantle cast
    Of kind affections finely wrought ?
Ah no ! the groundless thought were vain,
For so we ne'er can meet again !

May he who claims thy tender heart
    Deserve its love as I have done !
For, kind and gentle as thou art,
    If so beloved, thou 'rt fairly won.
Bright may the sacred torch remain,
And cheer thee till we meet again.

Wedding Day in Literature and Art

From "THE STORY OF AN AFRICAN FARM"

By OLIVE SCHREINER

"I DID n't know before you were so fond of riding hard," said Gregory to his little betrothed.

They were cantering slowly on the road to Oom Muller's on the morning of the wedding.

"Do you call this riding hard?" asked Em, in some astonishment.

"Of course I do! It's enough to break the horses' necks, and knock one up for the whole day besides," he added testily; then twisted his head to look at the buggy that came on behind. "I thought Waldo was such a mad driver; they are taking it easily enough to-day," said Gregory. "One would think the black stallions were lame."

"I suppose they want to keep out of our dust," said Em. "See they stand still as soon as we do."

Perceiving this to be the case, Gregory rode on.

"It's all that horse of yours: she kicks up such a confounded dust I can't stand it myself," he said.

Meanwhile the cart came on slowly enough.

. . . .

It was eight o'clock when they neared the farmhouse, a red brick building, with kraals to the right and a small orchard to the left. Already there were signs of unusual life and bustle; one cart, a waggon, and a couple of saddles against the wall betokened the arrival of a few early guests, whose numbers would soon be largely increased. To a Dutch country wedding guests start up in numbers astonishing to one who has merely ridden through the plains of sparsely inhabited karroo.

198

THE MARRIAGE PROCESSION.

Tidemand.

As the morning advances, riders on many shades of steeds appear from all directions, and add their saddles to the long rows against the walls, shake hands, drink coffee, and stand about in groups to watch the arriving carts and ox-waggons as they are unburdened of their heavy freight of massive Tantes and comely daughters, followed by swarms of children of all sizes, dressed in all manner of print and moleskin, who are taken care of by Hottentot, Kaffer, and half-caste nurses, whose many-shaded complexions, ranging from light yellow up to ebony black, add variety to the animated scene. Everywhere is excitement and bustle, which gradually increases as the time for the return of the wedding party approaches. Preparations for the feast are actively advancing in the kitchen; coffee is liberally handed round, and amid a profound sensation and the firing of guns, the horse-waggon draws up and the wedding party alight. Bride and bridegroom, with their attendants, march solemnly to the marriage-chamber, where bed and box are decked out in white with ends of ribbon and artificial flowers, and where on a row of chairs the party solemnly seat themselves. After a time bridemaid and best man rise, and conduct in with ceremony each individual guest, to wish success and to kiss bride and bridegroom. Then the feast is set on the table, and it is almost sunset before the dishes are cleared away and the pleasure of the day begins. Everything is removed from the great front room, and the mud floor, well rubbed with bullock's blood, glistens like polished mahogany. The female portion of the assembly flock into the side rooms to attire themselves for the evening, and reissue clad in white muslin, and gay with bright ribbons and brass jewelry. The dancing begins as the first tallow-candles are stuck up about the walls, the music coming from a couple of fiddlers in a corner of the room. Bride and bridegroom open the ball, and the floor is soon covered with whirling couples, and every one's spirits rise. The bridal pair mingle freely in the throng, and here and there a musical man sings vigorously as he drags his partner through the Blue Water or

John Speriwig; boys shout and applaud, and the enjoyment and confusion are intense, till eleven o'clock comes. By this time the children who swarm in the side rooms are not to be kept quiet longer, even by hunches of bread and cake; there is a general howl and wail that rises yet higher than the scraping of fiddles, and mothers rush from their partners to knock small heads together, and cuff little nursemaids, and force the wailers down into unoccupied corners of beds, under tables, and behind boxes. In half an hour every variety of childish snore is heard on all sides, and it has become perilous to raise or set down a foot in any of the side rooms lest a small head or hand should be crushed. Now, too, the busy feet have broken the solid coating of the floor, and a cloud of fine dust arises that makes a yellow halo round the candles, and sets asthmatic people coughing, and grows denser, till to recognise any one on the opposite side of the room becomes impossible, and a partner's face is seen through a yellow mist.

At twelve o'clock the bride is led to the marriage-chamber and undressed; the lights are blown out, and the bridegroom is brought to the door by the best man, who gives him the key, then the door is shut and locked, and the revels rise higher than ever. There is no thought of sleep till morning, and no unoccupied spot where sleep may be found.

From "VANITY FAIR"

By WILLIAM MAKEPEACE THACKERAY

ONE gusty, raw day at the end of April — the rain whipping the pavement of that ancient street where the old Slaughter's Coffee-house was once situated — George Osborne came into the coffee-room, looking very haggard and pale, although dressed rather smartly in a blue coat and brass buttons, and a neat buff waistcoat of the fashion of those days. Here was his friend Captain Dobbin, in blue and brass too, having abandoned the military frock and French-gray trousers, which were the usual coverings of his lanky person.

Dobbin had been in the coffee-room for an hour or more. He had tried all the papers, but could not read them. He had looked at the clock many scores of times; and at the street, where the rain was pattering down, and the people, as they clinked by in pattens, left long reflections on the shining stone; he tattooed at the table; he bit his nails most completely, and nearly to the quick (he was accustomed to ornament his great big hands in this way); he balanced the teaspoon on the milkjug; upset it, etc., etc.; and in fact showed those signs of disquietude, and practised those desperate attempts at amusement, which men are accustomed to employ when very anxious and expectant, and perturbed in mind.

Some of his comrades, gentlemen who used the room, joked him about the splendour of his costume and his agitation of manner. One asked him if he was going to be married. Dobbin laughed, and said he would send his acquaintance (Major Wagstaff of the Engineers) a piece of cake when that event took place. At length Captain Osborne made his appearance, very smartly dressed, but very pale and agitated, as we have said. He wiped his pale face with a large yellow bandana pocket-handkerchief that was prodigiously scented. He shook hands with Dobbin, looked at the clock, and told John, the waiter, to bring him some curaçoa. Of this cordial he swallowed off a couple of glasses with nervous eagerness. His friend asked with some interest about his health.

"Could n't get a wink of sleep till daylight, Dob," said he. "Infernal headache and fever. Got up at nine, and went down to the Hummums for a bath. I say, Dob, I feel just as I did on the morning I went out with Rocket at Quebec."

"So do I," William responded. "I was a deuce deal more nervous than you were, that morning. You made a famous breakfast, I remember. Eat something now."

"You 're a good old fellow, Will. I 'll drink your health, old boy, and farewell to — "

"No, no ; two glasses are enough," Dobbin interrupted him. "Here, take away the *liqueurs*, John. Have some cayenne-pepper with your fowl. Make haste, though, for it is time we were there."

It was about half an hour from twelve when this brief meeting and colloquy took place between the two captains. A coach, into which Captain Osborne's servant put his master's desk and dressing-case, had been in waiting for some time ; and into this the two gentlemen hurried under an umbrella, and the valet mounted on the box, cursing the rain and the dampness of the coachman who was steaming beside him. "We shall find a better trap than this at the church door," says he ; "that 's a comfort." And the carriage drove on, taking the road down Piccadilly, where Apsley House and St. George's Hospital wore red jackets still ; where there were oil lamps ; where Achilles was not yet born ; nor the Pimlico arch raised ; nor the hideous equestrian monster which pervades it and the neighbourhood — and so they drove down by Brompton to a certain chapel near the Fulham road there.

A chariot was in waiting with four horses ; likewise a

coach of the kind called glass coaches. Only a very few idlers were collected, on account of the dismal rain.

"Hang it!" said George, "I said only a pair."

"My master would have four," said Mr. Joseph Sedley's servant, who was in waiting; and he and Mr. Osborne's man agreed, as they followed George and William into the church, that it was a "reg'lar shabby turnhout; and with scarce so much as a breakfast or a wedding faviour."

"Here you are," said our old friend, Jos Sedley, coming forward. "You're five minutes late, George my boy. What a day, eh? Demmy, it's like the commencement of the rainy season in Bengal. But you'll find my carriage is water-tight. Come along, my mother and Emmy are in the vestry."

Jos Sedley was splendid. He was fatter than ever. His shirt-collars were higher; his face was redder; his shirt-frill flaunted gorgeously out of his variegated waistcoat. Varnished boots were not invented as yet; but the Hessians on his beautiful legs shone so, that they must have been the identical pair in which the gentleman in the old picture used to shave himself; and on his light green coat there bloomed a fine wedding favour, like a great white spreading magnolia.

In a word, George had thrown the great cast. He was going to be married. Hence his pallor and nervousness — his sleepless night and agitation in the morning. I have heard people who have gone through the same thing own to the same emotion. After three or four ceremonies, you get accustomed to it, no doubt; but the first dip, everybody allows, is awful.

The bride was dressed in a brown silk pelisse (as Captain Dobbin has since informed me), and wore a straw bonnet with a pink ribbon; over the bonnet she had a veil of white Chantilly lace, a gift from Mr. Joseph Sedley, her brother. Captain Dobbin himself had asked leave to present her with a gold chain and watch, which she sported on this occasion; and her mother gave her her diamond brooch — almost the only trinket which was left

to the old lady. As the service went on, Mrs. Sedley sat
and whimpered a great deal in a pew, consoled by the
Irish maid-servant and Mrs. Clapp from the lodgings.
Old Sedley would not be present. Jos acted for his father,
giving away the bride, whilst Captain Dobbin stepped up
as groomsman to his friend George.

There was nobody in the church besides the officiating
persons and the small marriage party and their attendants.
The two valets sat aloof superciliously. The rain came
rattling down on the windows. In the intervals of the
service you heard it, and the sobbing of old Mrs. Sedley in
the pew. The parson's tones echoed sadly through the
empty walls. Osborne's "I will" was sounded in very
deep bass. Emmy's response came fluttering up to her
lips from her heart, but was scarcely heard by anybody
except Captain Dobbin.

When the service was completed, Jos Sedley came forward and kissed his sister, the bride, for the first time for
many months — George's look of gloom had gone, and
he seemed quite proud and radiant. "It's your turn,
William," says he, putting his hand fondly upon Dobbin's
shoulder; and Dobbin went up and touched Amelia on
the cheek.

Then they went into the vestry and signed the register.
"God bless you, Old Dobbin," George said, grasping him
by the hand, with something very like moisture glistening
in his eyes. William replied only by nodding his head.
His heart was too full to say much.

"Write directly, and come down as soon as you can,
you know," Osborne said. After Mrs. Sedley had taken
an hysterical adieu of her daughter, the pair went off to
the carriage. "Get out of the way, you little devils,"
George cried to a small crowd of damp urchins, that were
hanging about the chapel door. The rain drove into the
bride and bridegroom's faces as they passed to the chariot.
The postilion's favours draggled on their dripping jackets.
The few children made a dismal cheer as the carriage,
splashing mud, drove away.

William Dobbin stood in the church porch, looking at it, a queer figure. The small crew of spectators jeered him. He was not thinking about them or their laughter.

"Come home and have some tiffin, Dobbin," a voice cried behind him, as a pudgy hand was laid on his shoulder, and the honest fellow's reverie was interrupted. But the captain had no heart to go a feasting with Jos Sedley. He put the weeping old lady and her attendants into the carriage along with Jos, and left them without further words passing. This carriage, too, drove away, and the urchins gave another sarcastical cheer.

"Here, you little beggars," Dobbin said, giving some sixpences amongst them, and then went off by himself through the rain. It was all over. They were married, and happy, he prayed God. Never since he was a boy, had he felt so miserable and so lonely. He longed with a heart-sick yearning for the first few days to be over, that he might see her again.

From "A BRIDAL SONG"

By HENRY HART MILMAN

TO the sound of timbrels sweet
   Moving slow our solemn feet,
We have borne thee on the road
To the virgin's blest abode;
With thy yellow torches gleaming,
And thy scarlet mantle streaming,
And the canopy above
Swaying as we slowly move.

Thou hast left the joyous feast,
And the mirth and wine have ceased,
And now we set thee down before
The jealously unclosing door,
That the favoured youth admits
Where the veilèd virgin sits
In the bliss of maiden fear,
Waiting our soft tread to hear,
And the music's brisker din
At the bridegroom's entering in,
Entering in, a welcome guest,
To the chamber of his rest.

From "BONAVENTURE: A PROSE PAS-TORAL OF ACADIAN LOUISIANA"[1]

By GEORGE W. CABLE

O N that instant the quiet of the village is broken by a sound of galloping hoofs.

Bonaventure stands still. How sudden is this change! He is not noticed now ; everything is in the highest animation. There are loud calls and outcries; children are shouting and running, and women's heads are thrust out of doors and windows. Horsemen come dashing into the village around through the lanes and up the street. Look! they wheel, they rein up, they throw themselves from the rattling saddles; they leave the big wooden stirrups swinging and the little unkempt ponies shaking themselves, and rush into the *boutique de* Monsieur Lichtenstein, and are talking like mad and decking themselves out on hats and shoulders with ribbons in all colours of the rainbow!

Suddenly they shout, all together, in answer to a shout outside. More horsemen appear. Lichtenstein's store belches all its population.

" La calege ! La calege ! " The caleche is coming! Something, he knows not what, makes Bonaventure tremble.

" Madame," he says in French to a chattering woman who has just run out of her door, and is standing near him tying a red Madras kerchief on her head as she prattles to a girl, — " madame, what wedding is this ? "

" *C'est la noce à* Zosephine," she replies, without looking at him, and goes straight on telling her companion how fifty dollars has been paid for the Pope's dispensation, because the bridal pair are first cousins.

---

[1] *By permission of Charles Scribner's Sons, from " Bonaventure," by George W. Cable. Copyright 1887 and 1888 by George W. Cable.*

Bonaventure moves back and leans against a paling fence, pallid and faint. But there is no time to notice him — look, look!

Some women on horseback come trotting into the street. Cheers! cheers! and in a moment louder cheers yet — the caleche with the bride and groom and another with the parents have come.

Throw open the church door!

Horsemen alight, horsewomen descend; down, also, come they that were in the caleche. Look, Bonaventure! They form by twos — forward — in they go. " Hats off, gentlemen! Don't forget the rule! — Now — silence! softly, softly; speak low — or speak not at all; sh-sh! Silence! The pair are kneeling. Hush-sh! Frown down that little buzz around the door! Sh-sh!"

Bonaventure has rushed in with the crowd. He cannot see the kneeling pair, but there is the curé standing over them and performing the holy rite. The priest stops; he has seen Bonaventure! He stammers and then he goes on. Here beside Bonaventure is a girl so absorbed in the scene that she thinks she is speaking to her brother, when presently she says to the haggard young stranger, letting herself down from her tiptoes and drawing a long breath:

" *La sarimonie est fait.*"

It is true; the ceremony is ended. She rises on tiptoe again to see the new couple sign the papers.

Slowly! The bridegroom first, his mark. Step back. Now the little bride — steady! Zosephine, *sa marque.* She turns; see her, everybody; see her! brown and pretty as a doe! They are kissing her. Hail, Madame 'Thanase!

" Make way, make way!" The man and wife come forth. — Ah! 'Thanase Beausoleil, so tall and strong, so happy and hale, you do not look to-day like the poor decoyed, drugged victim that woke up one morning out in the Gulf of Mexico to find yourself, without fore-intent or knowledge, one of a ship's crew bound for Brazil and thence to the Mediterranean! — " Make way, make

A Spanish Marriage.

Fortuny.

way!" They mount the caleches, Sosthene after Madame Sosthene; 'Thanase after Madame 'Thanase. "To horse, ladies and gentlemen!" Never mind now about the youth who has been taken ill in the chapel, and whom the curé has borne almost bodily in his arms to his own house. "Mount! mount! Move aside for the wedding singers!" — The wedding singers take their places, one on this side the bridal caleche, the other on that, and away it starts, creaking and groaning.

"Mais, arretez! — Stop, stop! Before going, *Passez le 'nisette!* — pass the anisette!" May the New Orleans compounder be forgiven the iniquitous mixture! "*Boir les dames avant!* — Let the ladies drink first!" Aham! straight from the bottle.

Now, go. The caleche moves. Other caleches bearing parental and grandparental couples follow. And now the young men and maidens gallop after; the cavalcade stretches out like the afternoon shadows, and with shouts and songs and waving of hats and kerchiefs, away they go! while from window and door and village street follows the wedding cry, —

"*Adjieu, la calege! Adjieu, la calege!* — God speed the wedding pair!"

Coming at first from the villagers, it is continued at length faint and far, by the attending cavaliers. As mile by mile they drop aside, singly or in pairs, toward their homes, they rise in their stirrups, and lifting high their ribbon-decked hats, they shout and curvette and curvette and shout until the eye loses them, and the ear can barely catch the faint farewell, —

"*Adjieu la calege! Adjieu les marriées!*"

Adieu; but only till the fall of night shall bring the wedding ball.

One little tune — and every Acadian fiddler in Louisiana knows it — always brings back to Zosephine the opening scene of that festive and jocund convocation. She sees again the great clean-swept seed-cotton room of a cotton-gin house belonging to a cousin of the ex-governor, lighted with many candles stuck into a perfect wealth of black bottles ranged along the beams of the walls. The fiddler's seat is mounted on a table in the corner, the fiddler is in it, each beau has led a maiden into the floor, the sets are made for the contra-dance, the young men stand expectant, their partners wait with downcast eyes and mute lips as Acadian damsels should, the music strikes up and away they go.

It was fine from first to last! The ball closed with the bride's dance. Many a daughter Madame Sosthene had waltzed the farewell measure with, and now Zosephine was the last. So they danced it, they two, all the crowd looking on : the one so young and lost in self, the other so full of years and lost to self, — eddying round and round each other in this last bright embrace before they part, the mother to swing back into still water, the child to enter the current of a new life.

And then came the wedding supper! At one end of the long table the bride and groom sat side by side, and at their left and right the wedding singers stood and sang. In each corner of the room there was a barrel of roasted sweet potatoes. How everybody ate that night! Rice! beef-balls ! Pass them here! pass them there! help yourself! reach them with a fork! *des riz ! des boulettes !* And the anisette ! bad whiskey and oil of anise — never mind that ; pour, fill, empty, fill again! Don't take too much — and make sure not to take too little! How merrily all went on !

On the Marriage of a Friend

"COMPOSED ON THE EVE OF THE MARRIAGE OF A FRIEND IN THE VALE OF GRASMERE, 1812"

By WILLIAM WORDSWORTH

WHAT need of clamorous bells, or ribbons gay,
　　These humble nuptials to proclaim or grace?
Angels of love, look down upon the place;
Shed on the chosen vale a sun-bright day!
Yet no proud gladness would the bride display
Even for such a promise: serious is her face,
Modest her mien; and she, whose thoughts keep pace
With gentleness, in that becoming way
Will thank you. Faultless does the maid appear;
No disproportion in her soul, no strife;
But when the closer view of wedded life
Hath shown that nothing human can be clear
From frailty, for that insight may the Wife
To her indulgent lord become more dear.

Wedding Day in Literature and Art

From "HE KNEW HE WAS RIGHT"

By ANTHONY TROLLOPE

THE Glascock marriage was a great affair in Florence; so much so that there were not a few who regarded it as a strengthening of peaceful relations between the United States and the United Kingdom, and who thought that the Alabama claims and the question of naturalisation might now be settled with comparative ease. An English lord was about to marry the niece of an American Minister to a foreign court. The bridegroom was not, indeed, quite a lord as yet, but it was known to all men that he must be a lord in a very short time, and the bride was treated with more than usual bridal honours because she belonged to a legation. She was not, indeed, an ambassador's daughter, but the niece of a daughterless ambassador, and therefore almost as good as a daughter. The wives and daughters of other ambassadors, and the other ambassadors themselves, of course, came to the wedding; and as the palace in which Mr. Spalding had apartments stood alone, in a garden, with a separate carriage entrance, it seemed for all wedding purposes as though the whole palace were his own.

The English Minister came, and his wife, — although she had never quite given over turning up her nose at the American bride whom Mr. Glascock had chosen for himself. It was such a pity, she said, that such a man as Mr. Glascock should marry a young woman from Providence, Rhode Island. Who in England would know anything of Providence, Rhode Island? And it was so expedient, in her estimation, that a man of family should strengthen himself by marrying a woman of family. It was so necessary, she declared, that a man when marrying should remember that his child would have two grandfathers, and would be called upon to account for four great-grandfathers. Nevertheless Mr. Glascock was — Mr. Glascock; and, let him marry whom he would, his wife would be the future Lady Peterborough. Remembering this, the English Minister's wife gave up the point, when the thing was really settled, and benignly promised to come to the breakfast with all the secretaries and attachés belonging to the legation, and all the wives and daughters thereof. What may a man not do, and do with éclat, if he be heir to a peer and have plenty of money in his pocket?

Mr. and Mrs. Spalding were covered with glory on the occasion; and perhaps they did not bear their glory as meekly as they should have done. Mrs. Spalding laid herself open to some ridicule from the English Minister's wife because of her inability to understand with absolute clearness the condition of her niece's husband in respect to his late and future seat in Parliament, to the fact of his being a commoner and a nobleman at the same time, and to certain information which was conveyed to her, surely in a most unnecessary manner, that if Mr. Glascock were to die before his father her niece would never become Lady Peterborough, although her niece's son, if she had one, would be the future lord. No doubt she blundered, as was most natural; and then the British Minister's wife made the most of the blunders; and when once Mrs. Spalding ventured to speak of Caroline as her ladyship, not to the British Minister's wife, but to the sister of one of the secretaries, a story was made out of it almost as false as it was ill-natured. Poor Caroline was spoken of as her ladyship backwards and forwards among the ladies of the legation in a manner which might have vexed her had she known anything about it; but, nevertheless, all the ladies prepared their best flounces to go to the wedding. The time soon would come when she would in truth be a " ladyship," and she might be of social use to any one of the ladies in question.

. . . .

. . . Everybody who was anybody in Florence was to be present. There were only to be four bridesmaids, Caroline herself having strongly objected to a greater number. As Wallach Petrie had fled at the first note of preparation for these trivial and unpalatable festivities, another American young lady was found; and the sister of the English secretary of legation, who had so maliciously spread that report about her " ladyship," gladly agreed to be the fourth.

.   .   .   .

It was generally admitted among the various legations in Florence that there had not been such a wedding in the City of Flowers since it had become the capital of Italia. Mr. Glascock and Miss Spalding were married in the chapel of the legation, — a legation chapel on the ground floor having been extemporised for the occasion. This greatly enhanced the pleasantness of the thing, and saved the necessity of matrons and bridesmaids packing themselves and their finery into close fusty carriages. A portion of the guests attended in the chapel, and the remainder, when the ceremony was over, were found strolling about the shady garden.

The whole affair of the breakfast was very splendid and lasted some hours. In the midst of the festivities the bride and bridegroom were whisked away with a pair of gray horses to the railway station, and before the last toast of the day had been proposed by the Belgian Councillor of Legation, they were half-way up the Apennines on their road to Bologna.

Mr. Spalding behaved himself like a man on this occasion. Nothing was spared in the way of expense, and when he made that celebrated speech, in which he declared that the republican virtue of the New World had linked itself in a happy alliance with the aristocratic splendour of the Old, and went on with a simile about the lion and the lamb, everybody accepted it with good humour in spite of its being a little too long for the occasion.

" It has gone off very well, mamma, has it not ? " said Nora, as she returned home with her mother to her lodgings.

" Yes, my dear; much, I fancy, as these things generally do."

" I thought it was so nice. And she looked very well. And he was so pleasant, and so much like a gentleman,— not noisy, you know, and yet not too serious."

" I dare say, my love."

" It is easy enough, mamma, for a girl to be married, for she has nothing to do but wear her clothes and look as pretty as she can. And if she cries and has a red nose it is forgiven her. But a man has so difficult a part to play. If he tries to carry himself as though it were not a special occasion, he looks like a fool that way ; and if he is very special, he looks like a fool the other way. I thought Mr. Glascock did it very well."

From "THE DIAMOND WEDDING" [1]

By EDMUND CLARENCE STEDMAN

RING! ring the bells and bring
    The people to see the marrying!
Let the gaunt and hungry and ragged poor
Throng round the great Cathedral door,
To wonder what all the hubbub 's for,
    And sometimes stupidly wonder
At so much sunshine and brightness, which
Fall from the church upon the rich,
    While the poor get all the thunder.

Ring! ring, merry bells, ring!
      O fortunate few
      With letters blue,
Good for a seat and a nearer view!
Fortunate few, whom I dare not name;
Dilettanti! Crême de la Crême!
We commoners stood by the street façade
And caught a glimpse of the cavalcade;
      We saw the bride
      In diamond pride,
With jewelled maidens to guard her side, —
Six lustrous maidens in tarlatan.
She led the van of the caravan;
    Close beside her, her mother
(Dressed in gorgeous *moire antique*
That told, as plainly as words could speak,
She was more antique than the other)
    Leaned on the arm of Don Rataplan

1 *By special permission of Houghton, Mifflin & Co.*
216

THE BRIDAL JEWELS.

Schachinger.

The Diamond Wedding

Santa Claus de la Muscovado
Señor Grandissimo Bastinado.
   Happy Mortal! fortunate man!
And Marquis of El Dorado.
In they swept, all riches and grace,
Silks and satins, jewels and lace;
In they swept from the dazzled sun,
And soon in the church the deed was done.
Three prelates stood on the chancel high:
A knot that gold and silver can buy
Gold and silver may yet untie,
   Unless it is tightly fastened;
What's worth doing at all's worth doing well.
And the sale of a young Manhattan Belle
   Is not to be pushed or hastened.

From "ROXY"[1]

By EDWARD EGGLESTON

THERE was nothing out of the ordinary about Roxy's wedding. There were present her aunt's family and Twonnet's; Miss Rachel Moore, who was to take her place as mistress of the house the next week, was there, of course, and Colonel Bonamy and his daughters, and as many besides as the old house would hold. Adams had asked Whittaker, but the minister had not come. Jemima stood in the background, the most impressive figure of all. The Methodist presiding elder, a venerable, white-haired man, familiarly called "Uncle Jimmy Jones," conducted the simple service.

I said there was nothing out of the ordinary. But Bobo was there. For days he had watched the cake-baking and the other preparations. He heard somebody say that Roxy was to be married, and he went about the house conning the saying like a lesson, as though he were trying to get some meaning out of it.

"Roxy is going to be married," he would say over and over, from morning till night. When he saw the company gathering, he went into an ecstasy of confused excitement. And when at last Roxy came into the room, in her simple bridal dress, he broke from his mother's side and seized Roxy's disengaged hand. Jemima and his mother made an effort to recapture him, but Roxy turned and said, "Let him come."

"Let him come," echoed Bobo, and walking by the side of the bride and her bridegroom till they halted in front of the minister, he looked up at the stately old man and said with childish glee, "Roxy's going to be married."

[1] *By permission of Charles Scribner's Sons, from "Roxy," by Edward Eggleston. Copyright by Charles Scribner's Sons, 1878.*

This outburst of Bobo's sent the colour of Mrs. Hanks's
face up to scarlet. What would the Bonamys think?
Jemima put her handkerchief over her mouth to stifle a
laugh, and Amanda Bonamy turned her head. Could n't
they keep the simpleton at home? The old minister was
confused for a moment, but the smile on Roxy's face reassured him. The lad stood still listening to the ceremony
and repeating it over in an inaudible whisper. When the
minister concluded the benediction with the words, " Be
with you evermore," Bobo caught at the last ' word and
cried : " Evermore, Roxy, evermore."

" Yes, Bobo, dear," said the bride, turning to him and
looking down into his wistful eyes. " Yes, evermore and
evermore."

Perhaps because they were embarrassed by this unexpected episode, the company were silent, while Bobo for a
moment turned over in his mind the word. Then by some
association he connected it with the last words of the prayer
Roxy had taught him. He went in front of her and looked
at her with the awed look he had caught from her in repeating his prayer, he pointed up as she had pointed in
teaching him, and said, —

" For ever and ever, amen."

" Yes, Bobo, for ever and ever, amen, and now you shall
have the very first kiss."

" The very first kiss," chuckled the innocent, as he
turned away after Roxy had kissed him.

Through all this interruption Adams stood by the long
clock and held on to the lapel of his coat firmly and de-
fiantly. He had a notion that the Bonamys thought that
their family lent a lustre to Roxy, and he wanted to knock
some of them over, but he kept firm hold of his coat and
contented himself with looking like a wild beast at bay.

Mrs. Hanks whispered to her husband that she felt as if
she could sink through the floor, and, indeed, she was quite
flustered when she came to wish the newly married " much
joy," and quite thrown out of the fine speech she had prepared for delivery to Mark. Amanda Bonamy kissed Roxy

condescendingly as became a well-bred girl; but when it came to Janet's turn, she kissed Roxy first on one cheek and then on the other, called her a dear, dear sister and said, —

"Was n't that sweet that poor little Bobo said? It made your wedding so solemn and beautiful, — just like your wedding ought to be."

And from that moment Roxy took the enthusiastic girl into her heart of hearts. She made her sit by her at the wedding dinner to make which had exhausted all the skill of Roxy and her helpers, and the whole purse of her father. For the custom of the time did not allow of coffee and sandwiches and cake passed around the room. As for light breakfasts and an immediate departure on a tour to nowhere in particular, that only came in with locomotives and palace-cars. In the good old days it cost as much to get married as it does now to be buried; one must then feed one's friends on fried chickens and roast turkeys and all sorts of pies and pound cake and "floating island" and "peach cobbler," — an enormous dish of pastry inclosing whole peaches, pits and all, — and preserves with cream, and grape jellies, and — But this is not a bill of fare.

There could be no wedding in a Hoosier village thirty or forty years ago without an infare on the following day. In those days the *faring* into the house of the bridegroom's parents was observed with great rejoicing. At an earlier stage of the village's history the little brass cannon was fired in honour of weddings, and almost the whole town kept holiday. On the day after Roxy's wedding Colonel Bonamy made a great infare, as became a great man like himself. It was preceded by a week of cooking and baking. On the day of the infare, "Uncle Billy," a skilful old negro, was imported from Kentucky to roast the pig which hung suspended by a wire in front of the wide kitchen fireplace, while Billy turned it round and round, basting it from time to time. For roast pig at a wedding feast was the symbol of aristocracy; a Bonamy might lose his soul, but he could not be married without a pig.

Roxy

Everybody who could be considered at all invitable was there. The Boones and Haz Kirtley's family and the fishermen's families and the poor whiteys generally were left out, but everybody who was anybody was there. Not only from town, but from the country and even from the Kentucky shore, guests were brought. Old Mother Tartrum was there, engaged in her diligent search after knowledge. She was in herself a whole Society for the Collection and Diffusion of Useless Information. She also collected various titbits of cake off the supper-table, which she wrapped in her red silk handkerchief and deposited in her pocket. She was a sort of animated Dictionary of Universal Biography for the town, able to tell a hundred unimportant incidents in the life of any person in the place, and that without being consulted.

.   .   .   .

Out of respect for Mark's and Roxy's scruples, and, too, for Mark's semi-clerical position as a " local " or lay preacher on his way to a further promotion into the " Travelling " ministry, there was no dancing. The company promenaded in the halls and up and down the gravel walks between the Lombardy poplars and among the sprucely trimmed pyramidal cedars that stood about the house.

From "ELDER PETTIGREW'S HELPMEET"[1]

By WILL CARLETON

ELDER PETTIGREW was married on the fifteenth
of July,
And some sixteen jealous maidens let their disappointment
fly;
And some seventeen other maidens scorned to give their
sorrow air,
And some eighteen other maidens laughed and said they
did n't care;
And some nineteen other maidens felt the fact come rather
near,
For the Elder's face was handsome, and his heart was full
of cheer.

And his older friends were sorry he had done as he had done,
For the bride was young and little, and retiring as a nun;
To be sure, her face was comely; still, she was n't much
to see,
And they had their own opinion what a pastor's bride
should be.
And they said, "Lone-handed pastors ought to search, and
search, and search,
Till they get a proper partner that can help them run the
church."

And she closed her eyes devoutly, or looked down upon
the floor,
When the fateful fact was mentioned that her maiden days
were o'er;

1 *From "City Festivals," published by Harper & Brothers.*

And her voice was just a flutter, and her answering
  timid-low ;
E'en her would-be rivals pitied, that she had to tremble so ;
But when once the fact was stated she was now the pastor's wife,
She glanced round upon the people with a newish lease of
  life.

From "THE WRECKER" [1]

By ROBERT LOUIS STEVENSON and LLOYD OSBORNE

TO fit out a schooner for sea, and improvise a marriage between dawn and dusk, involves heroic effort. All day Jim and I ran, and tramped, and laughed, and came near crying, and fell in sudden anxious consultations, and were sped (with a prepared sarcasm on our lips) to some fallacious milliner, and made dashes to the schooner and John Smith's, and at every second corner were reminded (by our own huge posters) of our desperate estate. Between whiles I found time to hover at some half-a-dozen jewellers' windows; and my present, thus intemperately chosen, was graciously accepted. I believe, indeed, that was the last though not the least of my concerns, before the old minister, shabby and benign, was routed from his house and led to the office like a performing poodle; and there, in the growing dusk, under the cold glitter of Thirteen Star, two hundred strong, and beside the garish glories of the agricultural engine, Mamie and Jim were made one. The scene was incongruous, but the business pretty, whimsical, and affecting; the typewriters with such kindly faces and fine posies, Mamie so demure, and Jim — how shall I describe that poor, transfigured Jim?

He began by taking the minister aside to the far end of the office. I know not what he said, but I have reason to believe he was protesting his unfitness; for he wept as he said it: and the old minister, himself genuinely moved, was heard to console and encourage him, and at one time to use this expression: "I assure you, Mr. Pinkerton, there are not many who can say so much" — from which I

WEDDED.

Leighton.

gathered that my friend had tempered his self-accusations with at least one legitimate boast.

From this ghostly counselling, Jim turned to me; and though he never got beyond the explosive utterance of my name and one fierce handgrip, communicated some of his own emotion, like a charge of electricity, to his best man. We stood up to the ceremony at last, in a general and kindly discomposure. Jim was all abroad; and the divine himself betrayed his sympathy in voice and demeanour, and concluded with a fatherly allocution, in which he congratulated Mamie (calling her " my dear ") upon the fortune of an excellent husband, and protested he had rarely married a more interesting couple.

At this stage, like a glory descending, there was handed in, *ex machina*, the card of Douglas B. Longhurst, with congratulations and four dozen Perrier-Jouet. A bottle was opened; and the minister pledged the bride, and the bridesmaids simpered and tasted, and I made a speech with airy bacchanalianism, glass in hand. But poor Jim must leave the wine untasted. " Don't touch it," I had found opportunity to whisper; " in your state, it will make you as drunk as a fiddler." And Jim had wrung my hand, with a " God Bless You, Loudon! — saved me again ! "

Hard following upon this, the supper passed off at Frank's with somewhat tremulous gaiety. And thence, with one-half of the Perrier-Jouet — I would accept no more — we voyaged in a hack to the " Norah Creina."

" What a dear little ship ! " cried Mamie, as our miniature craft was pointed out to her. And then, on second thought, she turned to the best man. " And how brave you must be, Mr. Dodd," she cried, " to go in that tiny thing so far upon the ocean ! " And I perceived I had risen in the lady's estimation.

The dear little ship presented a horrid picture of confusion, and its occupants of weariness and ill-humour. From the cabin the cook was storing tins into the lazarette, and the four hands, sweaty and sullen, were passing them from one to another from the waist. Johnson was three parts asleep over the table; and in his bunk, in his own cabin, the captain sourly chewed and puffed at his cigar.

" See here," he said, rising; " you 'll be sorry you came. We can't stop work if we 're to get away to-morrow. A ship getting ready for sea is no place for people, anyway. You only interrupt my men."

I was on the point of answering something tart; but Jim, who was acquainted with the breed, as he was with most things that had a bearing on affairs, made haste to pour in oil.

" Captain," he said, " I know we 're a nuisance here, and that you 've had a rough time. But all we want is that you should drink one glass of wine with us, Perrier-Jouet, from Longhurst, on the occasion of my marriage and Loudon's — Mr. Dodd's — departure."

" Well, it 's your lookout," said Nares. " I don't mind half an hour. Spell, O ! " he added to the men ; " go and kick your heels for half an hour, and then you can turn to again a trifle livelier. Johnson, see if you can't wipe off a chair for the lady."

. . . .

The little party in the cabin, so disastrously begun, finished, under the mellowing influence of wine and woman, in excellent feeling and with some hilarity. Mamie, in a plush Gainsborough hat and a gown of wine-coloured silk, sat, an apparent queen, among her rude surroundings and companions. The dusky litter of the cabin set off her radiant trimness : tarry Johnson was a foil to her fair beauty ; she glowed in that poor place, fair as a star ; until even I, who was not usually of her admirers, caught a spark of admiration ; and even the captain, who was in no courtly humour, proposed that the scene should be commemorated by my pencil. It was the last act of the evening. Hurriedly as I went about my task, the half hour had lengthened out to more than three before it was completed : Mamie in full value, the rest of the party figuring in outline only, and the artist himself introduced in a back view, which was pronounced a likeness. But it was to Mamie that I devoted the best of my attention; and it was with her I made my chief success.

"Oh!" she cried, "am I really like that? No wonder Jim . . ." She paused. "Why, it's just as lovely as he's good!" she cried : an epigram which was appreciated, and repeated as we made our salutations, and called out after the retreating couple as they passed away under the lamp-light on the wharf.

From "OFF THE SKELLIGS" [1]

By JEAN INGELOW

A T last Wednesday came. I woke, and could hardly believe it. We breakfasted precisely as usual; then the two children and their parents set off on foot to the quiet little church, and Giles and I followed over two or three fields. We sat down on a grassy bank, to put on some new gloves; they were not white, however, and I, though I wore a white dress, as I usually did in the morning, had no other bridal array. I did not even then believe that all would go well. I had a vivid recollection of the telegrams; but we rose, and he took me on to the church, — a little rural building that stood open. There I saw Mr. Crayshaw, who had come from London to give me away, — and no one else at all, but Mr. Mompesson with his white gown on, and Mrs. Mompesson with the children.

The ceremony actually began, and I perceived, almost to my surprise, that we certainly were being married, after all! But as if it was quite impossible that anything concerning me could be done as other people do it, all on a sudden, while Giles held my hand, a thought seemed to flash straight out of his heart into mine, that he had forgotten the ring. I was quite sure of it; he did not even put his finger into his waistcoat pocket, as a man might have done who had bought one and left it behind. There *was* no ring; he had forgotten it.

A pause.

"Fanny," said Mr. Mompesson; and Mrs. Mompesson, with all the good-will in the world, and with Mr. Crayshaw to help her, tried to get her ring off her dear, fat, friendly hand, and tried in vain.

Giles almost groaned. He had expected me to be more than commonly nervous; now seemed some ground for it;

but real and sheer nervousness often goes off when there is anything to be nervous about, and now I felt very much at my ease, and whispered to Giles that a ring would be found somewhere. So it was. The clerk had darted out of the church at the first sight of Mrs. Mompesson's hand, and in a few minutes he returned, followed by a lovely, fresh-complexioned, young woman in a linen sunbonnet, with a fat, crowing baby on her arm. She was out of breath, and coming up to Giles quickly, she thrust out her honest hand, and allowed him to draw her ring off, and marry me with it. A healthy-looking young fellow, in a paper cap, which he presently removed, came slouching in after her, and looked on, unable, as it seemed, to repress an occasional grin of amusement ; and when the ceremony was over, they followed us into the vestry, and we all sat talking a little while, till some rings were brought from a shop for me, and Giles chose one and paid for it. Then I felt that I was Mrs. Brandon.

He returned the ring he had used to the young woman, but I observed that she made her husband put it on for her again ; and as he did so, he remarked to Giles, with a certain quaint complacency, that wives wanted humouring ; and for his part (he might be wrong) he considered it was their due. Then in all good faith, assuring him that he would never repent what he had that day done, he set his paper cap on his head, and retired with his family, while we, having taken leave of our friends, stepped out into the fields, and departed together to begin our story.

Wedding Day in Literature and Art

From "SUSAN'S ESCORT" [1]

By EDWARD EVERETT HALE

THEY had no minister at New Padua, or rather he had a sore throat, and was studying evolution at Halle. So our Father Lawrence went over there to marry them. All the people went over. Strangest of all, Mrs. Montague went over.

"Not that I go willingly," she said to Effie at the last moment, as the girl arranged some magnificent diamonds which Romayne had given his mother; "I do not go willingly, and no one thinks I go willingly. But who knows? They may be married by the bishop. They were never very sound. Then there·must be some one to give my son away."

For Mrs. Montague leans to the third primitive secession, and is doubtful about other rituals than her own. So she went to her martyrdom. She herself saw to the toilets of her daughters, in a fashion, so that these wretched girls at the Hoods' should not in any sort eclipse them. How many there were she did not know, she said; she believed they made up most of the scholars. Her own "exhibit," as the managers of fairs say, was perfect. Her coachman Michael was in a new livery with an immense favour. Otto was on the box with Michael, with a bigger favour. Only Fritz was in Mrs. Montague's carriage; and the girls, with Romayne, were in their own carriage behind, with Anders as grand as Michael, and François with him on the box, each with gorgeous favours. Even the horses had favours covering the blinders, which the grooms had compelled the chambermaids to make for them. Then, in that great drag which the Montagues sent to the station for their guests, followed every man and woman of the staff of

1 From "Susan's Escort," published by Harper & Brothers.

A Russian Marriage Toilet.

Makowsky.

the house. Actually old Katy, the housekeeper, who had carried Romayne to the font when he was baptised, locked the side door, and put the key in her pocket. For there was not one person in that house who would stay away from Romayne's wedding. Had Mrs. Montague stayed, I do not know who would have got her supper.

" I should have been frightened out of my skin," said she.

And at the seminary everything was elegant and just right. It was " ever so pretty." Since Mrs. Hood bought the Flinder's lot, and made her own avenue through the maples, the approach to the house has been " about as fine as they make." To-night this was blazing with electric light, and the designs for the illumination, without being showy, were all convenient, pretty, and, to us country people, wholly new. The greenhouse must have been emptied, I should have said, such was the show of plants at the entrance. But afterwards, when I took Bianca in there to get a part of this story from her and to have " a little conversation," I did not see but it was as brilliant as ever. Anyway, we entered through a tropical garden. I saw that dried-up Mr. Roger from the apothecary store, and Hugh Roger by him. Juliet had not forgotten her old friends.

We were shown to various disrobing-rooms by pretty maids, who had little favours of orange-blossoms. Strauss's orchestra from New York was playing music so ravishing that I would have pardoned Father Lawrence if the service all went out of his head as he listened. Romayne came up with me and some of the other fellows. He made his sister carry in for Juliet the great blue box which held her bouquet.

A minute more and Effie came out again, blushing her prettiest, and said, " Juliet wants to see you, Ro."

And Ro went into that mysterious bride-chamber, which he had never seen before. And there stood his own dear girl, wonderful and gracious. Her veil lay across a great table waiting for the bridesmaid to put it on her at the last moment. The damask in which Madam Mifflin, her great-grandmother, had been married, had been dug out of a Ginevra chest. Madam Mifflin's skeleton was not found with it, for she lived to dance at Madison's second inauguration. This brocade was to be worn to-night. And Romayne said, " Oh, my darling, I 'm afraid to kiss you."

" Never fear that," said she. " We will do it again when I am ninety to remember to-night by."

" It seemed to me," said he, " that the day would never be done."

" But it is, you see. When will you learn to be reasonable? Romayne, when you say such things I am afraid for you."

" Afraid for me, Juliet? "

" I am afraid that you will forget that the pressure increases with the squares, and even with the cubes, and if your lower ranges are to stand it long, you must put in heavier tubing."

" Oh, now you can laugh; you may say anything," said the happy fellow, only wondering that she chose to chaff him just now.

" You goose!" said she; " do you not know why I have called you? "

" I hoped you called me to marry me," said he, ruefully.

" I called you to explain to you the mystery."

" My darling, you are so beautiful I forgot there was a mystery."

" That is enough," said Juliet. " I thought you were perfect; now I know you are. All the more shall you know." Then, with a tragic pause, " Do you see this key? Do you see yon door? Open it." And she stood silent, not quite daring to look up.

Romayne opened the door. Within was a perfect plumber's equipment, — pincers, clippers, big solderers, little solderers, bismuth strip, superstrip, substrip, saws, augers, test-bottles, cinnamon and rose-water, piping of every size, — all were there.

" Romayne, your own Juliet does the plumbing for the seminary. This is my mystery — and my mother's."

From "THOU HAST SWORN BY THY GOD, MY JEANIE"

By ALLAN CUNNINGHAM

THOU hast sworn by thy God, my Jeanie,
    By that pretty white hand o' thine,
And by a' the lowing stars in heaven,
    That thou wad aye be mine !
And I hae sworn by my God, my Jeanie,
    And by that kind heart o' thine,
By a' the stars sown thick owre heaven,
    That thou shalt aye be mine.

Then foul fa' the hands that wad loose sic bands,
    And the heart that wad part sic luve!
But there 's nae hand that can loose my band,
    But the finger o' Him abuve.
Though the wee, wee cot maun be my bield,
    And my claething ne'er sae mean,
I wad lap me up rich i' the faulds o' luve, —
    Heaven's armfu' o' my Jean.

From "A COLONIAL WOOING"[1]

By CHARLES CONRAD ABBOTT, M.D.

A S John Bishop had said, the proposed wedding had caused a dissension, and several members of the meeting had expressed themselves so freely that serious trouble was feared. John did not attend, even on First-day, but calmly awaited the decision of a new committee to whom the whole matter was referred. What he feared would be the case resulted. There was a division; and if he and Ruth were married on the chosen day and at Pearson's they would be subject to discipline, and the question of legality might arise: was the wedding in accordance with the customs of Friends? And if not, and no magistrate was present, or hireling priest performed the ceremony, might not trouble be the outcome, and their opponents triumph in a manner to blight their whole lives? John could stand anything for her sake, but was powerless to alter the decision of the constituted authorities. No wonder he was sorely troubled.

"Please don't set me wild by all this law and custom and so on," said Ruth, when Robert placed the matter before her. "What does John say? How should I know? But oh, dear, I did want it to be on my birthday, as John and I planned. And if it's wrong one day, why not another?" And Ruth threatened to treat the Pearsons to an hysterical scene which her cousin Robert neatly avoided by saying,—

"There is a difference in the matter."

"Is there? Do some think it would be right? Then tell John I side with them, and let the matter 'go to court,'

[1] *By permission of J. B. Lippincott Co., from "A Colonial Wooing," by Charles Conrad Abbott.*

do you call it? afterwards," exclaimed Ruth, with more enthusiasm than calm judgment and added, "But what do you think, Cousin Robert? Tell me that."

"That it will come out all right, Fairie; but I'm no judge or man of the law."

"You're enough of a one for me, if John's willing;" and with this decision preparations for the wedding rapidly proceeded.

．　　．　　．　　．　　．　　．　　．　　．　　．

The day was perfect; such a one as, in this region,[1] can only come in the month of May. Pearson's orchard and the apple-trees that lined his lane were in full bloom, and the huge wild crab-tree, with its wealth of roseate blossoms, perfumed the air for a long distance. Millions of busy bees were humming among the flowers, and the birds that through the winter had been far away were now again in their summer homes and rejoicing as these returned wanderers always do. The best features of the year were spread in profusion, and with the clear blue sky, with peaceful clouds floating peacefully across it, combined to make a most fitting background for the ending of long weeks of anxiety and pain and the beginning of a lifetime, let us hope, of unalloyed pleasure.

By noon the neighbours generally had congregated about the Pearson mansion, and after the usual greetings and comments they gathered in the spacious parlour, that needed to-day no interior decoration, though this was not lacking, as every window was open and the flowers were peeping in, and the merriest birds posted themselves on the nearest bushes. When the guests were seated, a short silence ensued, and then were heard footsteps and the rustling of silk and satin. John Bishop and Ruth entered the room, and, occupying the chairs reserved for them, sat facing the company. Then silence again, only broken at last by John rising and holding out his hand to Ruth, who also rose and said those words of mighty import that for ever bound him

[1] Province of Pennsylvania, in the year 1695.

to her. She made like promises to him, and they were married.

. . . .

The marriage certificate, brought under protest and not likely to be accepted, was signed by those present, but lacked the one signature that Ruth most highly prized, — her mother's. Then the restraint of formality and of solemnity fell away, and the buzz and hum of many voices filled the room. There was now an end to the mystery, and the good people of the valley must find some other subject for discussion and wondering. While the excitement was at its height and every one was talking as if not to his fellow, a little incident caused a momentary pause. For reasons she alone could explain, but many correctly surmised, the Watsons had not been present. Now, her daughter married, she was free to come to her cousin's house, and as she entered the room, Ruth saw her mother the first time since the day of her departure for England.

There was a quick exclamation of joy, and in another moment the words " Mother," " Ruth," heard only by those nearest, they were in each other's arms. John Bishop stood by with folded arms and a look of triumph lighting his handsome face, the proudest and happiest man in the province.

Elizabeth

From "ELIZABETH" [1]

By HENRY WADSWORTH LONGFELLOW

THEN John Estaugh came back o'er the sea for the
gift that was offered,
Better than houses and lands, the gift of a woman's
affection.
And on the First-day that followed, he rose in the Silent
Assembly,
Holding in his strong hand a hand that trembled a little,
Promising to be kind and true and faithful in all things.
Such were the marriage rites of John and Elizabeth Estaugh.

[1] *By special permission of Houghton, Mifflin & Co.*

Wedding Day in Literature and Art

From "THE ROMANCE OF A JESUIT MISSION: A HISTORICAL NOVEL"[1]

By M. BOURCHIER SANFORD

"AND now, Father, I would speak of our marriage," said Godfrey. "We hope, we believe, that you will consent that it take place to-morrow before we set out on our return."

"To-morrow! Wait, rather, until our arrival in Quebec."

"To-morrow, Father, as you know, we part from Leon de Charolais when he begins his lonely journey to seek the Hurons on the North Shore. It is our wish that he should be with us; for Dorothy has a deeper regard for her brother Leon than for any one else upon the earth — save myself."

"Is this your wish, Leon?" asked the Superior, gently.

"It is my heartfelt wish, Father."

"Then, my son, it shall be granted. We will set up our altar in yonder grove. Doubtless the fair bride will not regret that her garments are but of rough material."

"Reverend Father, my mother has sent to her many garments of goodly texture. We have carried them with difficulty over rough ways."

"Will your parents be satisfied that you should be joined in marriage by one not of their faith?"

"They will, Father."

When the Superior had questioned Godfrey and was satisfied that he and his betrothed had been baptised, he appointed for the two certain meditations and prayers to precede the sacrament of matrimony, and directed the

[1] By permission of the Baker & Taylor Co., from " The Romance of a Jesuit Mission," by M. B. Sanford.

CONGRATULATIONS.

Erdmann.

lover to permit the fair girl to withdraw and remain for some hours in retreat.

Then the good news was sent out, and the women were bidden to begin to make ready a marriage feast, and deck a bridal bower in a grove.

. . . .

In the morning the bridal bower was seen, decked with wild flowers. There were crimson roses and white lilies from the forest, and from an abandoned beaver meadow had come scarlet lobelias, calceolarias, — white, pink, yellow, and crimson, — wild iris, tiger lilies, and trilliums.

To Nialona had been given the honour of dressing the bride. Here and there on the soft white dress and veil she had fastened a spray of roses and ferns; and a rose blush tinged the cheeks that had been so pale.

The Huron women, who had never beheld anything so beautiful as that bridal dress, were as children in their surprise and delight. And priests and laymen alike gratified the bridegroom by the assertion that a lovelier maid had never been wedded.

Dorothy stood alone with De Charolais, and looked into his face with her joy lighting her beautiful eyes. " O, my Brother Leon, my true and noble Brother Leon," she said, " why must you, who have brought happiness to us, live and suffer alone? And yet, yet, there is something in your face, in your eyes that I never saw there before. It reminds me of words I once heard my — my father read, ' A Conqueror returning from his wars.' "

" Do not sorrow for me, my Sister Dorothy. If it be possible, let me hear of you; you will be happy; in that I shall find happiness. May all marriage blessings be granted you; joy and peace and no regrets."

. . . Ragueneau said the words that made Dorothy Wynne and Godfrey Dermount man and wife. By the Superior's direction she gave as her maiden name that of her adopted parents.

At the wedding feast — the noon dinner of which all

partook before setting out on the journey — it was notice-able that De Charolais was as full of life and interest as any one at the board.

· · · · · · · · ·

Presently Dorothy and her husband took their places in their canoe over which Bernard Gautier and the Huron boys had made a canopy to protect the bride from the glare of the summer sun.

As they went down the river, they looked back many times to wave their last adieux to Leon, who stood with Wenekin on the lonely shore.

Figs and Thistles

From "FIGS AND THISTLES"[1]

By ALBION W. TOURGEE

A LL day, about the streets and in the stores and offices of Lanesville, there had been strange, vague rumours in regard to the gifted preacher who had so delighted all the day before. It was hard to tell whence they had come, or what they were, but they all pointed to the church and to that night as the time and place where some startling *dénouement* was to be made.

Since morning, Markham Churr's bays had been going hither and thither, flashing the bright sleigh, with its gay trimmings and abundant robes, around in a hundred unexpected places. The hour for the evening service arrived. The old pastor sat alone in the high pulpit. The house was crowded. The gallery as well as the body of the house was full. People sat upon the steps of the pulpit and around the altar. Chairs were placed in one of the aisles, and it was quickly filled. Every one was on the lookout for something, he knew not what. Those who sat in the seats before and behind the pastor's pew plied his poor wife with questions, which she could no more answer than her inquisitors, —

Where was Mr. Worthington? Had she seen him that day? Was his name really Worthington? How did he come to be Colonel? Why was he not in the pulpit? Why were not the Churrs there? And a hundred more, of similar import, until the poor woman could only reply, —

" Don't ask me! I don't know! I don't know! "

It was a vast relief to her when the brazen tongue of the bell hushed the busy ones of her neighbours, and with

[1] *By permission of Fords, Howard & Hulbert, from " Figs and Thistles,"* *by A. W. Tourgee.*

its last echoes her husband rose in the pulpit and read the opening hymn. He was very pale, and seemed much affected. Every seat in the house was full except General Churr's — no one sat there. Whether it was by arrangement, or because their family were so seldom absent that no one else had been put in there, no one seemed to know. Yet every one looked at it — some ominously and with a shake of the head which bespoke unutterable mystery, and others just wonderingly.

The town of Lanesville might be said to have collected in the church. Not only this, but there were a great number from Aychitula. It seemed that the fame of the young preacher had reached there, and a large number had made their curiosity, as it seemed, an excuse to try the fine sleighing by a moonlight ride. Among these were four old people, for whom, at their two houses, a sleigh had called at a late hour, the driver of which declared there was no mistake. He had been especially directed to drive them to Lanesville to hear the great Western preacher, and return the next day. He declared that the team was already paid for, and the arrangements for their comfort made, though he refused to disclose the name of his employer. So, after much consultation, the old neighbours had consented to accept the favour of their unknown friend, and the ride from Aychitula had not been merrier to any of the young hearts who made it that night than to those hearty old people who sat side by side on the front seat in the little church, waiting in mute wonder to hear the preacher who was not present.

The service proceeded and the old pastor poured out his heart in prayer. His tender, almost tearful, tones were scanned with curious criticism by his watchful auditors, who thought they might gather from his words the secret which they felt was in his heart, in his voice, in the very air, only so vague and evanescent that they could not quite catch its form and outline. The prayer is finished, the Scripture lesson read, and yet the mystery is not defined. The air is charged with a mysterious electricity, yet they cannot trace its currents. Then comes the text, and the wondering auditors look into each other's puzzled eyes, as they admit their inability to see its application to the state of facts which had tacitly come to be presumed by every one, though hardly whispered by the boldest, —

"What God hath cleansed, call not thou common or unclean."

The sermon is finished. From text unto conclusion it has been watched with the keenest scrutiny by every auditor. Nothing has been detected, however, except a humble tenderness, as if the old pastor had but recently been with Fisherman Peter, in his vision, when the great white sheet was let down from Heaven and had heard the gentle reproof which came from out the rifted cloud after it was withdrawn. The touch of God's finger had sanctified all mankind to him. Unconsciously, his hearers forgot what so many of them were seeking for, and, by the lips of his servant, the Nazarene taught again to willing hearts the one great truth of his dispensation, — the Brotherhood of Man.

Hearts which came to criticise were touched and softened, and many a one not wont to pray joined fervently in the closing petitions. Eyes were moist and lips were tremulous in that congregation, for the tongue of flame rested above many a soul.

So hushed and solemn were the hearts of his hearers, that when, after the prayer, he said, " We will now celebrate the holy ordinance of marriage," and then picked his way among the crowded worshippers to the front of the altar, the audience manifested no great surprise or undue interest ; they had so far forgotten the curiosity which possessed them at first. But suddenly they saw, half-way up the aisle on the left, the form of the new preacher, with Amy Levis upon his arm, while behind them came General Churr and his wife, looking happier than their oldest friends remembered to have seen them ! To say that the excitement was intense from that instant would but ill describe it. All rose to their feet, and waited, in anxious expectancy, for — no one knew what, but every one felt that the secret they had waited for so long was about to be revealed.

When they finally stood before the altar, the old pastor said, in soft, benignant tones, and with a look that he must have caught from some ascending angel in his most rapt visions, —

"We are about to celebrate the marriage of Frank Worthington Horton and Amy Levis. If any of you know any just cause why this man and this woman may not be lawfully joined together, let him now speak, or for ever after hold his peace."

He had purposely varied the form, spoken the names with unusual distinctness and a meaning emphasis; but no one uttered a word. The mystery for which they had been seeking was now within their grasp, but the words of the preacher were still in their ears and every tongue was hushed. Tears were in very many eyes. Our four old friends in the front pew — the parents of the bride and of the groom — seemed too stunned to realise the full meaning of what was taking place.

The ceremony was quickly over. A few noticed that the bridegroom was as pallid as the snow without, and others that wifely care already sat upon the brow of the bride. Then they passed down the aisle, and the voice of Markham Churr was heard requesting the audience to remain seated for a few moments. As soon as they had passed out, he said, —

"Neighbours, you have seen a strange thing, — the beautiful outcome of a life whose fruitage many a heart in this house feared. As Colonel Frank Worthington, he who has just gone forth has a thousand times redeemed Frank Horton's fault. Yet so stricken does he feel that he is anxious to escape from you here and bury himself once more in the Great West. He has given you a surprise to-night. Will you come to my house to-morrow night and surprise him, whom I am glad to call my friend, with a greeting which shall make his old father young again and shame his distrust of your goodness?"

Figs and Thistles

There was a little cheer and a general cry of " Yes!
yes !"

" At seven o'clock, then; and we will shake that left
hand until he will wish more than ever for the right which
he lost at Chickamauga."

Nothing could stop the cheer then, and when the old
pastor gave out the doxology, it was sung with the jubilant
clangour of Miriam's triumph-song; and the benediction
which came after it was like the promise of life to the
Apostles on the Mount of Transfiguration.

Wedding Day in Literature and Art

From "THE VILLAGE RECTOR"

By HONORÉ DE BALZAC

IN the month of April formal invitations were sent to all Graslin's circle of acquaintance.

At eleven o'clock one fine sunny morning a caleche and a brougham, drawn by Limousin horses in English harness (old Grossetête had superintended his colleague's stable), arrived before the poor little shop where the dealer in old iron lived; and the excited quarter beheld the bridegroom's sometime partners and his two clerks.

There was a prodigious sensation, the street was filled by the crowd eager to see the Sauviats' daughter. The most celebrated hairdresser in Limoges had set the bride's crown on her beautiful hair and arranged her veil of priceless Brussels lace; but Veronique's dress was of simple white muslin.

A sufficiently imposing assembly of the most distinguished women of Limoges was present at the wedding in the cathedral; the Bishop himself, knowing the piety of the Sauviats, condescended to perform the marriage ceremony. People thought the bride a plain-looking girl.

For the first time she entered her hôtel, and went from surprise to surprise.

A state dinner preceded the ball, to which Graslin had invited almost all Limoges.

The dinner given to the Bishop, the prefect, the president of the court of first instance, the public prosecutor, the mayor, the general and to Graslin's sometime employers and their wives, was a triumph for the bride, who, like all simple and unaffected people, proved unexpectedly charming. None of the married people would dance, so that Veronique continued to do the honours of her house,

246

and won the esteem and good graces of most of her new acquaintances; asking old Grossetête, who had taken a great kindness for her, for information about her guests, and so avoiding blunders. During the evening the two retired bankers spread the news of the fortune, immense for Limousin, which the parents of the bride had given her.

From "THE STORY OF A NEW YORK HOUSE"[1]

By H. C. BUNNER

AND in May of the next year, King's Bridge being out of the question, and etiquette being waived at the universal demand of society, the young couple stood up in the drawing-room of the Dolph house to be wed.

The ceremony was fashionably late, seven o'clock in the evening. And after it was over, and the young couple had digested what St. Paul had to say about the ordinance of wedlock, and had inaudibly promised to do and be whatever the dominie required of them, they were led by the half-dozen groomsmen to the long glass between the front windows, and made to stand up there, with their faces toward the company, and to receive the congratulations of a mighty procession of friends, who all used the same formulas, except the very old ones, who were delicately indelicate.

The bridegroom wore a blue coat and trousers, and a white satin waistcoat embroidered with silver-threaded roses and lilies-of-the-valley. The coat was lined with cream-coloured satin, quilted in a most elaborate pattern; and his necktie was of satin, too, with embroidered ends. His shirt was a miracle of fine linen. As to the bride, she was in white satin and lace, and at her throat she wore a little bunch of late white columbines, for which Mr. Jacob Dolph the younger had scoured the woods near Fort Washington.

There was to be a grand supper later; and the time of waiting was filled up with fashionable conversation.

. . . .

It was all over at last, and old black Julius, who had been acting as a combination of link boy and major-domo

1 *By permission of Charles Scribner's Sons, from " The Story of a New York House," by H. C. Bunner. Copyright, 1887, by Charles Scribner's Sons.*

INTRODUCING THE BRIDE.
Erdmann.

at the foot of the front steps, extinguished his lantern, and went to bed, some time before a little white figure stole up the stairs and slipped into a door that Chloe — black Chloe — held open.

And the next day Jacob Dolph the elder handed the young bride into the new travelling carriage with his stateliest grace, and Mr. and Mrs. Jacob Dolph, junior, rolled proudly up the road, through Bloomingdale, and across King's Bridge — stopping for luncheon at the Des Anges house — over to New Rochelle, where the feminine head of the house of Des Anges received them at her broad front door, and where they had the largest room in her large, old-fashioned house, for one night. Madame Des Anges wanted to keep them longer, and was authoritative about it. But young Jacob settled the question of supremacy then and there with the utmost courtesy, and Madame Des Anges, being great enough to know that she was beaten, sent off the victor on the morrow, with his trembling accomplice by his side, and wished them *bon voyage* as heartily as she possibly could.

So they started afresh on their bridal tour, and very soon the travelling carriage struck the old Queen Anne's road and reached Yonkers. And there, and from there up to Fishkill, they passed from one country-house to another, bright particular stars at this dinner and at that supper, staying a day here and a night there, and having just the sort of sociable, public, restless, rattling good time that neither of them wanted.

At every country-house where they stayed a day they were pressed to stay a week, and always the whole neighbourhood was routed out to pay them social tribute. The neighbours came in by all manner of conveyances. One family of aristocrats started at six o'clock in the morning, and travelled fourteen miles down the river in an ox-cart, the ladies sitting bolt upright, with their hair elaborately dressed for the evening's entertainment. And once a regular assembly ball was given in their honour at a town-hall, the use of which was granted for the purpose specified

by unanimous vote of the town council.   Of course, they
had a very good time; but then there are various sorts of
good times.   Perhaps they might have selected another sort
for themselves.

There is a story that, on their way back, they put up for
several days at a poor little hostelry under the hills below
Peekskill, and spent their time in wandering through the
woods and picking wild-flowers; but it lacks confirmation,
and I should be sorry to believe that two well-brought-up
young people would prefer their own society to the un-
limited hospitality of their friends in the country.

THE BRIDESMAIDS.

Williams.

The Bridesmaid

"THE BRIDESMAID"

ALFRED, LORD TENNYSON

O BRIDESMAID, ere the happy knot was tied,
    Thine eyes so wept that they could hardly see;
Thy sister smiled and said, " No tears for me !
A happy bridesmaid makes a happy bride."
And then, the couple standing side by side,
Love lighted down between them full of glee,
And over his left shoulder laugh'd at thee,
" O happy bridesmaid, make a happy bride."
And all at once a pleasant truth I learned,
For while the tender service made thee weep,
I loved thee for the tear thou couldst not hide,
And prest thy hand and knew the press returned,
And thought, " My life is sick of single sleep :
O happy bridesmaid, make a happy bride."

From "A WOMAN HATER"

By CHARLES READE

THEY were married in St. George's Church very quietly, by special licence. . . . But Vizard was too old-fashioned, and too proud of his wife to sneak into Vizard Court with her. He did not make it a county matter; but he gave the village such a *fête* as had not been seen for many a day. The preparations were intrusted to Mr. Ashmead, at Ina's request.

" He will be sure to make it theatrical," she said; " but perhaps the simple villagers will admire that, and it will amuse you and me, love; and the poor dear old Thing will be in his glory — I hope he will not drink too much."

Ashmead was indeed in his glory. Nothing had been seen in a play that he did not electrify Islip with, and the surrounding villages. He pasted large posters on walls and barn doors, and his small bills curled round the patriarchs of the forest and the roadside trees and blistered the gate-posts.

A soapy pole with a leg of mutton on high for the successful climber. Races in sacks. Shot blindfold races with wheelbarrows. Pig with a greased tail to be won by him who could catch him and shoulder him without touching any other part of him; bowls of treacle for boys to duck heads in and fish out coin; skittles, ninepins, aunt sally, etc., etc., etc.

But what astonished the villagers most was a May-pole, with long ribbons, about which ballet-girls undisguised as Highlanders danced, and wound and unwound the parti-coloured streamers, to the merry fiddle, and then danced a reel upon a platform, then returned to their little tent; but out again and danced a hornpipe undisguised as Jacky Tars.

THE MARRIAGE PROCESSION.

Heipfer.

A Woman Hater

Beer flowed from a sturdy regiment of barrels. "The Court" kitchen and the village bake-house kept pouring forth meats, baked, boiled, and roast; there was a pile of loaves like a hay-stack; and they roasted an ox whole on the green; and when they found they were burning him raw, they fetched the butcher, like sensible fellows, and dismembered the giant, and so roasted him reasonably.

In the midst of the revelling and feasting, Vizard and Mrs. Vizard were driven into Islip village in the family coach, with four horses streaming with ribbons.

They drove round the Green, bowing and smiling in answer to the acclamations and blessings of the poor, and then to Vizard Court. The great doors flew open. The servants, male and female, lined the hall on both sides, and received her bowing and courtesying low, on the very spot where she had nearly met her death; her husband took her hand and conducted her in state to her own apartment.

It was open house to all that joyful day, and at night magnificent fireworks on the sweep, seen from the drawing-room by Mrs. Vizard, Miss Maitland, Miss Gale, Miss Dover, and the rosy-cheeked curate whom she had tied to her apron-strings.

At two in the morning Mr. Harris showed Mr. Ashmead to his couch. Both gentlemen went up the stairs a little graver than any of our modern judges, and firm as a rock; but their firmness resembled that of a roof rather than a wall; for these dignities as they went made one inverted V — so, Λ.

From "LOVE ME LITTLE, LOVE ME LONG"

By CHARLES READE

I HAVE already noticed that Lucy, after capitulation, laid down her arms gracefully and sensibly. When she was asked to name a very early day for the wedding, she opposed no childish delay to David's happiness, for the " Rajah " was to sail in six weeks and separate them. So the licence was got, and the wedding day came ; and all Lucy's previous study of the contract did not prevent her from being deeply affected by the solemn words that joined her to David in holy matrimony. She bore up, though, stoutly ; for her sense of propriety and courtesy forbade her to cloud a festivity. But when the postchaise came to convey bride and bridegroom on their little tour, and she had to leave Mrs. Wilson and Eve for a whole week, the tears would not be denied ; and, to show how perilous a road matrimony is, these two risked a misunderstanding on their wedding day, thus : Lucy, all alone in the post-chaise with David, dissolved — a perfect Niobe — gushing at short intervals. Sometimes a faint explanation gurgled out with the tears : " Poor Eve ! her dear little face was working so, not to cry. Oh ! oh ! I should not have minded so much if she had cried right out."

Then again it was, " Poor Mrs. Wilson ! I was only a week with her, for all her love. I have made a c-at's p-paw of her — oh ! "

Then again, " Uncle Bazalgette has never noticed us ; he thinks me a h-h-h-ypocrite." But quite as often they flowed without any accompanying reason.

Now, if David had been a poetaster, he would have said : " Why these tears ? She has got me. Am I not more than an equivalent to these paltry considerations ? " and all this salt water would have burned into his vanity like liquid caustic. If he had been a poet, he would have said : "Alas! I make her unhappy whom I hoped to make happy;" and with this he would have been sad, and so prolonged her sadness, and perhaps ended by sulking. But David had two good things, — a kind heart, and a skin not too thin; and such are the men who make women happy, in spite of their weak nerves and craven spirits.

He gave her time; soothed her kindly; but did not check her weakness dead short.

At last my lady Chesterfield said to him penitently, "This is a poor compliment to you, Mr. Dodd;" and then Niobised again, partly, I believe, with regret that she was behaving so discourteously.

"It is very natural," said David, kindly, "but we shall soon see them all again, you know."

Presently she looked into his radiant face, with wet eyes, but half a smile. "You amaze me; you don't seem the least terrified at what we have done."

"Not a bit," cried David, like a cheerful horn : "I have been in worse peril than this, and so have you. Our troubles are all over, I see nothing but happiness ahead."

He then drew a sunny picture of their future life, to all which she listened demurely, and in short, he treated her little feminine distress as the summer sun treats a mist that tries to vie with it. He soon dried her up, and when they reached their journey's end she was as bright as himself.

Wedding Day in Literature and Art

From "MAUD MELVILLE'S MAR-RIAGE"[1]

By E. EVERETT-GREEN

I HARDLY know when it was that I was definitely told that I was to marry Rupert whilst we were still children, but the consciousness that the vaguely meditated plan was taking shape forced itself upon me quite early in the spring of the year 1682 (the year in which I was married); and as I knew little enough of the political troubles surging round us, I thought it a curious time to choose, because Rupert was going to be taken from England quite soon.

.   .   .   .

I do not remember my wedding day itself so well as the day that preceded it. I know that the household seemed astir from an early hour, and that everybody was bustling and excited. I had been awake quite a long time the preceding night, and I slept late on into the next morning, and nobody came to arouse me. So that when I did at last wake up, it was almost time for me to be dressed for the ceremony.

We were to be married in a little chapel in connection with one of Sir Charles Melville's manors. These private chapels, with their beautiful architecture and stained glass windows, seemed somewhat Popish in mother's eyes; and this particular little chapel was one of the very few places of the kind that had escaped the destructive zeal of the Roundhead soldiers. It was almost perfect still; and I was pleased to be married there, for Rupert and I were very fond of the little place, and would often visit it

1 *By permission of Thomas Nelson & Sons, from " Maud Melville's Marriage," by E. Everett-Green.*

together, where he would tell long tales of his ancestors who lay sleeping in the vault beneath.

Nurse Gowrie and mother both came to dress me in my wedding clothes. I do not know if I was considered a pretty child, but I remember feeling a glow of satisfaction as I beheld my reflection in a mirror on my way down to the hall. I was twelve years old and tall for my age, and my eyes were dark and bright, and my skin pale and clear. My hair was short and curled round my head; but it was to grow long now that I was married, Nurse Gowrie said, and to-day my curls were concealed under a sort of coronet and white veil, of which I felt very proud. My little sisters were also in white, and they looked very pretty, I thought. Cottingham and Oliver had walked on in advance, but father and mother and we girls went in the family coach, which rumbled very leisurely along, and jolted a great deal, for the roads were always very full of holes and lumps.

I remember being married very well. I was not at all frightened, and I looked about me with some curiosity when I was not required to speak or to attend very particularly.

There were a good many finely dressed people in the chapel, some of whom I knew and some of whose faces were strange. One of these faces fascinated me a great deal. It belonged to a man very richly dressed and a complete stranger to me. His skin was very dark and sallow; his features were strongly marked, and seemed in a way familiar, though I could not imagine where I could have seen him. He stood beside Sir Charles Melville, looking on with a negligent air of amusement at the scene.

When the ceremony was concluded, and a little buzz of talk began among the bystanders, this dark stranger moved forward, everybody making way for him with an air of deep respect.

" By my troth, young lad, but you have won a fair bride for yourself. I must beg a kiss from those rosy lips; " and he bent forward, half-laughing, as if he meant to kiss me. But I drew back a little, and answered boldly: "I belong to Rupert now. I shall not kiss anybody unless he allows me to."

" Odds fish ! but she has a spirit of her own, this bride of yours ! She will assert herself one of these fine days, and you will have need to look to yourself," laughed the stranger, whilst all around stood dead silent, and Rupert whispered quickly and hurriedly, —

" Kiss him, Maud ; kiss his hand. It is the king ! "

At that I felt frightened and knelt down to kiss his hand, as I had seen people do in the few pictures we possessed of court life. But the king only laughed louder, and held me up and kissed my forehead ; and then he linked his arm within that of my Lord Halifax and went out of the church with him, laughing and talking.

After that I remember very little about my wedding day, though I know that we had a banquet in the hall, and that the tenants and the poor people were feasted in the park, the weather being very warm and dry. I never heard clearly how it was that the king had come to be there. I do not think mother quite liked it, and I heard no more about it at all. Indeed my thoughts were now almost entirely taken up with Rupert's speedy departure, and I was sad at heart in the thought of losing my husband and play-fellow, whom I loved very dearly in my childish way.

FROM "COUNSEL TO GIRLS"

BY ROBERT HERRICK

THEN be not coy, but use your time,
    And, while ye may, go marry ;
For having lost but once your prime,
    You may for ever tarry.

Wedding Day in Literature and Art

From "THE LOVELY WANG: A BIT OF CHINA"[1]

By THE HON. LEWIS WINGFIELD

IN consternation, giddy, with swimming head and grop-
ing hands, the bride-elect — face to face with Fate —
staggered from Wang's presence into the arms of a posse of
women. What female is there in any land whose blood is
not warmed by a wedding? Although circumstances of a
peculiar nature would have to be considered, the new member of the Wang family was to be tied up in the Foh-Kien
fashion with as much solemnity as might be.

Intricate preparations had been going forward for several
days in secret, while unconscious Chu was moping. Chu
had always intended to flee if matters came to a crisis without succour appearing from without; and yet, now that, like
a summer thunder-clap, the stroke had come, he was irre-
sistibly tickled by the absurdity of his predicament, while
alarmed at possible results.

As to fleeing it was out of the question; for was he
not caged fast in the inner apartments, surrounded by a
score of women? A marriage between two men could in
no sense be binding; that was a comfort. How the rickety
groom was to be got to the Hall of Ancestors was to the
bride a marvel. Sure he would fall to pieces on the way.
If the farce must be played out, it must. After the ceremony the groom would be packed off to bed again; and
then — good-bye! His affectionate spouse would take the
earliest opportunity to show a clean pair of heels.

But, ah! the barbed shaft that smote the heart of Chu!
The world would be black, the sun extinguished; for he
would see Plumbloom no more! The pang of the thought
was harrowing, but, I regret to record, on this occasion

1 By permission of the Publishers' Plate Renting Co.

transitory; for at this moment Wen-Chi produced with becoming gravity the bridal robes, and Chu burst into a shout of laughter.

An indecorous bride, to behave with levity on this the most serious occasion of her life! An eccentric bride! For, seizing the dress and crown of coral and feathers, she skipped with great strides into her room, and hooked the door behind her. The venerable nurse was scandalised. Lightness of heart is good in season. Dear, dear! What a time they were all like to have of it when this strange matron should assume the reins of government!

It was almost dark when Miss Hung emerged and permitted the tirewomen to complete the work. Her attire was worthy of the occasion. Strings of amber, carnelian, and pearls in alternate rows covered her breast. Her robe was like the first blush of morning trimmed with fragments of the moon. Her eyebrows were like the tea-leaf, her lips like the scarlet azalea. Her numberless ornaments went tinkle, tinkle, as she walked, her shoes were shaped like the phœnix, while a perfume of musk and ambergris was freely diffused around. Not that the heroine of the evening could be permitted to walk far. Oh, dear, no.

Wrapped in an immense red mantle and veil, with a hat as large as a mandarin's umbrella, she was boxed in a red *hwa-kiau*, which, being locked by the nurse, was borne on the shoulders of four men, and, mid salvos of crackers, deposited in the Hall of Ancestors. By the dim light of paper lanterns, the mandarin stood there, with his son by his side, surrounded by the magnates of the prefecture. There was a banging of drums, a too-tooing of flageolets, a waving of wooden dragons' heads and official insignia.

The youngest gentleman carried the roast pork, and held it aloft on a stick as the groom, with six obeisances, took from the nurse the key and unlocked the prison of his bride. Hand in hand, she still in hat and mantle, they moved along the line of family tablets, making three bows to each. Then flinging themselves down before Mr. Wang, they solemnly vowed, in presence of the dead, to be

faithful till the summons of Death. Then two cups of
wine, joined by a scarlet thread, were handed by a little
child ; and the gentleman unveiling the lady by a graceful
jerk, the twain pledged each other, while music struck up
again, and there was another discharge of crackers. Thus
were the forms of a Foh-Kien marriage properly complied
with, and the pair were man and wife.

But now the *sin fujin*, or new chatelaine, began what is
to many a painful ordeal. Unveiled by her husband, she
had to stand with her hands before her to undergo the
criticisms of the crowd. They audibly discussed her nose,
suggesting to Nature improvements to be wrought out in
the next specimen ; and so all-engrossing was the amusement that for some time nobody perceived the advent of
another guest, who, fluttering a-tiptoe, stood trembling in
the rear. Mrs. Wei — at last — too late ! Her eyes did
not deceive her. Oh, luckless day ! Oh, fell disaster !
What is done may not be undone ! How blamably dila-
tory had been the elder Hung ! There was no doubt of
the terrific fact ! His son was Mrs. Wang !

As, unobserved herself, she stood silently watching, a thrill
passed down the spine of the White Ant, and she rubbed
her blear eyes, scarce believing what she saw. Yes ! No !
Could it be ? Great Heaven ! By the fitful light of crackers, she noticed the husband's hand.

All Chinese hands are small and long ; but this one was
unduly tiny, more fragile than the one it held. The truth
flashed upon her, and she groaned. Diamond cut diamond,
indeed. 'T was not a mock marriage, but a real one. If the
bride was a man, the groom was a woman ! They were tied
fast enough. Chu was not Mrs. Wang. Miss Wang was
Mrs. Hung. Which was it ? This way lunacy ! Did
Chu know it ? Was he himself deceived ? What would
the merchant say when the dread news was broken ? Who
would break it — she, Mrs. Wei ? Never ! She would far
rather perish. After all the lectures about espousing an
heiress ! Most horrible of all — what would Granny say
— the gruesome tyrant ? Chu must be mad.

The Well of St. Keyne

From "THE WELL OF ST. KEYNE"

By ROBERT SOUTHEY

A TRAVELLER came to the well of St. Keyne;
    Pleasant it was to his eye,
For from cock-crow he had been travelling,
    And there was not a cloud in the sky.

.   .   .   .

There came a man from the neighbouring town
    At the well to fill his pail,
On the well-side he rested it,
    And he bade the stranger hail.

.   .   .   .

" St. Keyne," quoth the countryman, " many a time
    Drank of this crystal well,
And before the angel summoned her
    She laid on the water a spell.

" If the husband of this gifted well
    Shall drink before his wife,
A happy man thenceforth is he,
    For he shall be master for life.

" But if the wife should drink of it first,
    Heaven help the husband then ! "
The stranger stooped to the well of St. Keyne,
    And drank of its waters again.

" You drank of this well, I warrant, betimes ? "
　He to the countryman said.
But the countryman smiled as the stranger spake,
　And sheepishly shook his head.

" I hastened as soon as the wedding was done,
　And left my wife in the porch.
But i' faith she had been wiser than me,
　For she took a bottle to church."

Edwin Brothertoft

From "EDWIN BROTHERTOFT"[1]

By THEODORE WINTHROP

IT was agreed among all the gossips of the Province —
and the gossips were right — that this was not a mer-
cenary match. Youth and beauty on both sides, what
could be more natural than love and marriage ? And then
the gossips went on to weigh the Brothertoft name against
the Billop fortune, and to pronounce — for New York in
those days loved blood more than wampum — that the
pounds hardly balanced the pedigree. Both parties were in
deep mourning. Of course there could be no great wedding. But all the female quality of the province crowded
to Trinity Church to see the ceremony. The little boys
cheered lustily when the Billop coach, one of the three or
four in town, brought its broadside to bear against the
church porch, and, opening its door, inscribed with the
Billop motto, " Per omnia ad opes," discharged the blushing bridegroom and his bride.

The beadle — for beadles have strutted on our soil —
quelled the boys and ushered the happy pair to the chancel
rail. It is pleasant to know that the furniture of the altar,
reading-desk and pulpit, which met their eyes, was crimson
damask " of the richest and costliest kind," and cost in
England forty-two pounds eleven shillings and three-
pence.

Venerable Rector Barclay read the service with a slight
Mohawk accent. He had been for some years a mission-
ary among that respectable tribe, — not, be it observed, the
unworthy offshoot known as Mohocks and colonised in
London, — and had generally persuaded his disciples to
cut themselves down from polygamy to bigamy. Rever-

1 *By permission of the Publishers' Plate Renting Co.*

end Samuel Auchmuty assisted the Rector with occasional interjections of Amen.

The great officials of the Province could not quit business at this hour; but the Patroons who happened to be in town mustered strong in honour of their order. Of pretty girls there came galore. Pages would fail to name them and their charms. There was the *espiègle* Miss Jay of that fine old Huguenot Protestant stock which still protests pertinaciously against iniquity in Church and State. There was the sensible Miss Schuyler, the buxom Miss Beekman, high-bred Miss Van Rensselaer, Miss Winthrop, faultless in toilette and temper, Miss Morris, wearing the imperious nose of the family, popular Miss Stuyvesant, that Amazonian filly, Miss Livingston, handsome Mary Phillipse with her determined chin, Julia Peartree Smith, *nez en l'air*, as usual, and a score of others, equally fair, and equally worthy of a place in a fashionable chronicle.

" Poor Edwin Brothertoft ! " said the Peartree Smith, as the young ladies filed out after the ceremony. " Did you hear that bold creature make her responses, ' I Jane take thee Edwin,' as if she were hailing the organ loft ? These vulgar girls understand the policy of short engagements. They don't wish to be found out. But company manners will not last for ever. Poor Mr. Brothertoft ! Why could he not find a mature woman ? " (Julia had this virtue, perhaps, to an exaggerated degree, and had been suspected of designs on the bridegroom.) " Girls as young as she is have had no chance to correct their ideal. She will correct it at his expense. She will presently find out he is not perfect, and then will fancy some other man would have suited her better. Women should have a few years of flirtation before they settle in life. These pantalette marriages never turn out well. An engagement of a few weeks to that purse-proud baby, her father's daughter ! Poor Edwin Brothertoft ! He will come to disappointment and grief."

With this, Miss Julia, striving to look Cassandra, marches off the stage.

But Edwin Brothertoft had no misgivings. If he had fancied any fault of temper in his betrothed, or perceived any divergence in principle, he had said to himself, " My faithful love shall gently name the fault, or point the error, and her love shall faithfully correct them."

The Billop coach rumbled away on its little journey down Wall Street. Parson Barclay bagged his neat fee and glowed with good wishes. The world buzzed admiration. The little boys huzzaed. The bell-ringer tugged heartily at the bell-rope. And at every tug of his, down on the noisy earth, the musical bells, up in the serene air, responded, " Go, happy pair! All bliss, no bale! All bliss, no bale! "

The rumble of the " Leathern conveniency," the applause of young New York, and the jubilation of the bells were so loud that Edwin was forced to lean very close to his wife's cheek while he whispered, —

" We were alone, and God has given us each a beloved companion. We are orphans; we shall be all in all to one another. Long, long, and always brightening years of thorough trust and love, dearer than was ever dreamed, lie before us. How happy we shall be in our glowing hopes! how happy in our generous ambitions! how happy in our earnest life! Ah, my love! how can I love you enough for the gift of this beautiful moment, for the promise of the fairer times to come! "

From "NORWOOD; OR, VILLAGE LIFE IN NEW ENGLAND"[1]

By HENRY WARD BEECHER

A SOFT cloud had hid the moon. It began to move away. The light shone out again.

"Barton, I do not believe you mean to tell me, after all. What is the shamefaced secret?"

"You will smile, I know. But I feel it. I want every one that has been with me in danger and trouble to be present in my great joy to-morrow. Colonel Stanton, who befriended me after I was a prisoner after Bull Run, has come. The Hetheringtons are all in your house. Rose, my horse, that carries a man's heart in him, that never flinched under fire, that was wounded as well as I, that carried me along the hardest journeys unflagging, and saved me several times from captivity,— I want him near me when I am married. I know that to many it would sound foolish. But no one but a soldier can know a soldier's feeling for a faithful horse."

"No one but a soldier and a soldier's wife," replied Rose. "You ought to be ashamed of being ashamed of such a feeling. He shall stand in golden shoes, and eat the plumpest oats out of a china vase, if it will please you, Barton."

"It is only a feeling, but it is as strong as superstition. Of course it is not for his sake, but for my own. I shall feel better if he stands in front of the yard where I can see him."

. . . .

The day broke over the hills, bent evidently on being present at the wedding. It came in golden tresses, and in

[1] *By permission of Fords, Howard, & Hulbert, from "Norwood," by Henry Ward Beecher.*

A MARRIAGE.

Bayard.

silver vapours, and infinite jewelry of dew, and it lit up the
world with joy as it came; but Rose and Barton forgot, as
they stood in the arbor, that there was anybody happy
but themselves. Could it be possible that there was any
joy left?

Dr. Wentworth was as calm, outwardly, as if only the
usual business was going on. His face shone. His voice
was lower and richer than usual. His eye carried in it a
perpetual benediction.

The great mansion was vocal in every room. Guests
were present from the east and west and south. The town
swarmed with friends come to the wedding. 'Biah Cathcart renewed his youth, and Rachel's face shone with
unexpressed thanksgiving. Hiram Beers was glorious.
Why not? As he had gone to Dr. Wentworth's to live,
in a neat cottage built expressly for him, and to have full
charge of the Doctor's stables, barn, and place, why should
he not consider this occasion as a family matter?

Pete Sawmill was triumphant. Great was the honour
and glory that came back with him to Norwood. The
story of his simple affection and fidelity was known to all,
and all agreed with Deacon Trowbridge, " that Pete ain't
much in the intellects, but he's got a heart as big as an
ox."

And nobody was surprised to learn that Pete was to live
with Barton Cathcart for life; nor that he appeared on this
morning with a bran-new suit of broadcloth, and that he
had a red cord sewed the whole length of the side seams
of his pantaloons, and that he wore military buttons on his
coat and vest. Pete hankered after these vanities, and it
was not believed that, if he was pleased, anybody else
would be hurt. . . . Throughout the great wedding day,
Pete carried himself most becomingly, dividing his attention during the ceremony between Barton and Barton's
war-horse. He was much disappointed when Barton, after
the ceremony, did not mount and repeat some of the brilliant feats of horsemanship which he had seen him perform. But supposing that, for some good reason, Barton

had changed his mind, he led the scarred horse back to his oats.

At noon, when all the company were assembled, and everybody was merry, chatting and chattering, all at once the church bell broke out into the most musical of invitations. To be sure, its duty was to ring at twelve, every day. But any one could tell that there was more than that in it to-day. Its paternal soul had a wedding thought in it. It was no measured, doctrinal ring, fit for Sunday. It was no fearful funeral ring, thick and heavy. It was a real, out-springing, merry ring, as that of a bell that would like to kick up its heels and dance on the green with the best of them.

Before the bell had done ringing a movement was seen about Dr. Wentworth's mansion. From the front door issued first Dr. Buell and a brother clergyman, then came Dr. and Mrs. Wentworth, and then came Rose and Barton; (while the boys that were looking in at the gate nodded to each other and said, " By George, jest look at that ! ain't they bunkum ? ") and then came Agate Bissell, and all the other members of the family; and after them flocks and crowds of friends. They moved down to the great elm-tree, which hung down its paternal arms about them and filled all its top with blessings. There, at length, stood Rose and her husband, under the flickering shadows and checkered golden light that had amused her when a babe. While Parson Buell prayed, all the birds in the tree-top made responses and said amen ! Then there was a moment's pause. There stood the noble pair. By Barton's side stood Will Belden on one leg and a crutch. On Rose's side stood Rose Hetherington, " too pretty for anything," said several young gentlemen near by. Then, in the simple forms of the good times, the ceremony proceeded; and Parson Buell, at its close, laid his hands upon their heads, bowed to his touch, and blessed them. And they were blessed !

No salutation of mere ceremony followed. Barton turned to Rose with an embrace that seemed like to have merged her into himself. Rose put her arms with full love about her husband. For a second they stood folded, some words they whispered, and there were few dry eyes that looked on them. Even Judge Bacon wiped his eyes, and declared that " it was remarkably good, positively affecting, and so unexpected, too."

There was but one event that befell the party which filled them with astonishment, and that was the sudden and unexpected decease of Agate Bissell. None out of Dr. Wentworth's family even knew that she was ailing, that under a fair appearance a hidden fire was in her heart that would surely take away her name from among those who had so long known it and loved it.

She had manifested, while Rose's wedding service proceeded, a tremulousness, as of one consciously weak, but who had determined not to give way till Rose was married. But Agate could hold out no longer. Scarcely had Rose received the salutations of her own kindred before her father called her aside and her husband also, and quite a stir and excitement arose among the crowd as Dr. Buell, with some dignity and firmness, as if repressing a nervous tremble, approached Agate Bissell, and taking her by the hand, walked to the very place where Rose and Barton had been standing, and stood before the excited crowd, who wondered that even at a wedding Parson Buell should venture on such a bold jest. Then came forth Parson Edwards Dwight Bigelow, with whom Buel had many a night held glorious wassail of theology, discussing till after midnight whether sin was born in the nature of a child or began only when developed by action; what was the nature of generous and right actions anterior to a saving change ; whether conversion stood in the act of choice on the sinner's part, or was an irresistible and efficacious influence exerted upon him *ab extra*. Over these and kindred savoury delights they had dissipated many a night.

There stood Parson Buell and Agate Bissell, and made answer to the solemn interrogatories, and she gave away her name, and with a blush as tender and beautiful as if she were just seventeen, she accepted her bridal kiss from Dr. Buell.

Deacon Marble was all a-tremble. The tears ran down his cheeks. " I wonder what Polly would have given to have seen this day. I guess she thinks she died too soon. Howsomever she could n't help it. Well, well, well,— Agate, you 've took us in this time. This is the best one yit ! I dew say, when I saw Parson Buell a-kissin' you, I sort of shivered all over. But you stood it beautiful. But no merit, you know, no merit, cos I s'pose you 're used to it, eh ? "

Agate, who really looked queenly, replied, —

" Why, Deacon Marble, my husband never kissed me before in his life."

" You don't say, now! I can't hardly b'lieve that. Dr. Buell is a nice and strict man. But courtin', you know, and engaged, why kissin' is accordin' to natur, and grace, too. I kissed Polly a hundred times afore I married her, and you say that Buell never kissed Agate Bissell before ? "

" Yes ; I believe he kissed Agate *Bissell*, but he never kissed Agate *Buell* before."

This quite overthrew the good deacon — he laughed immoderately, and repeated the story to every one on the ground, as an instance of remarkable wit.

Silas Marner

From "SILAS MARNER"

By GEORGE ELIOT

THERE was one time of the year which was held in Raveloe to be especially suitable for a wedding. It was when the great lilacs and alburnums in the old-fashioned gardens showed their golden and purple wealth above the lichen-tinted walls, and when there were calves still young enough to want bucketfuls of fragrant milk. People were not so busy then as they must become when the full cheese-making and the mowing had set in; and besides, it was a time when a light bridal dress could be worn with comfort and seen to advantage.

Happily the sunshine fell more warmly than usual on the lilac tufts the morning that Eppie was married, for her dress was a very light one. She had often thought, though with a feeling of renunciation, that the perfection of a wedding dress would be a white cotton, with the tiniest pink sprig at wide intervals; so that when Mrs. Godfrey Cass begged to provide one, and asked Eppie to choose what it should be, previous meditation had enabled her to give a decided answer at once.

Seen at a little distance as she walked across the church-yard and down the village, she seemed to be attired in pure white, and her hair looked like the dash of gold on a lily. One hand was on her husband's arm, and with the other she clasped the hand of her father Silas.

"You won't be giving me away, father," she had said before they went to church; "you'll only be taking Aaron to be a son to you."

Dolly Winthrop walked behind with her husband; and there ended the little bridal procession.

There were many eyes to look at it, and Miss Priscilla Lammeter was glad that she and her father had happened

to drive up to the door of the Red House just in time to
see this pretty sight. They had come to keep Nancy company to-day, because Mr. Cass had to go away to Lyerly,
for special reasons. That seemed to be a pity, for otherwise he might have gone, as Mr. Crackenthorpe and Mr.
Osgood certainly would, to look on at the wedding feast
which he had ordered at the Rainbow, naturally feeling a
great interest in the weaver who had been wronged by one
of his own family.

"I could ha' wished Nancy had had the luck to find a
child like that and bring her up," said Priscilla to her
father, as they sat in the gig; "I should ha' had something young to think of then, besides the lambs and the
calves."

"Yes, my dear, yes," said Mr. Lammeter; "one feels
that as one gets older. Things look dim to old folks:
they'd need have some young eyes about 'em to let 'em
know the world's the same as it used to be."

Nancy came out now to welcome her father and sister;
and the wedding group had passed on beyond the Red
House to the humbler part of the village.

Dolly Winthrop was the first to divine that old Mr.
Macey, who had been set in his arm-chair outside his own
door, would expect some special notice as they passed,
since he was too old to be at the wedding feast.

"Mr. Macey's looking for a word from us," said Dolly;
"he'll be hurt if we pass him and say nothing — and him
so racked with rheumatiz."

So they turned aside to shake hands with the old man.
He had looked forward to the occasion, and had his pre-
meditated speech.

"Well, Master Marner," he said in a voice that quavered
a good deal, "I've lived to see my words come true. I
was the first to say there was no harm in you, though your
looks might be again' you; and I was the first to say
you'd get your money back. And it's nothing but right-
ful as you should. And I'd ha' said the 'Amens,' and
willing, at the holy matrimony; but Tookey's done it a

good while now, and I hope you'll have none the worse luck."

In the open yard before the Rainbow the party of guests were already assembled, though it was still nearly an hour before the appointed feast time. But by this means they could not only enjoy the slow advent of their pleasure; they had also ample leisure to talk of Silas Marner's strange history, and arrive by due degrees at the conclusion that he'd brought a blessing on himself by acting like a father to a lone motherless child. Even the farrier did not negative this sentiment: on the contrary, he took it up as peculiarly his own, and invited any hardy person present to contradict him. But he met with no contradiction; and all differences among the company were merged in a general agreement with Mr. Snell's sentiment that when a man had deserved his good luck, it was the part of his neighbours to wish him joy.

As the bridal group approached, a hearty cheer was raised in the Rainbow yard; and Ben Winthrop, whose jokes had retained their acceptable flavour, found it agreeable to turn in there and receive congratulations; not requiring the proposed interval of quiet at the Stone-pits before joining the company.

Eppie had a larger garden than she had ever expected there now; and in other ways there had been alterations at the expense of Mr. Cass, the landlord, to suit Silas's larger family. For he and Eppie had declared that they would rather stay at the Stone-pits than go to any new home. The garden was fenced with stones on two sides, but in front there was an open fence, through which the flowers shone with answering gladness, as the four united people came within sight of them.

"Oh, father," said Eppie, "what a pretty home ours is! I think nobody could be happier than we are."

From "MR. GILFIL'S LOVE–STORY"

By GEORGE ELIOT

O N the 30th of May, 1790, a very pretty sight was
seen by the villagers assembled near the door of
Foxholm Church. The sun was bright upon the dewy
grass, the air was alive with the murmur of bees and the
thrilling of birds, the bushy blossoming chestnuts and the
foamy flowering hedgerows seemed to be crowding round
to learn why the church bells were ringing so merrily, as
Maynard Gilfil, his face bright with happiness, walked out
of the old Gothic doorway with Tina on his arm. The
little face was still pale, and there was a subdued melancholy in it, as of one who sups with friends for the last
time, and has his ear open for the signal that will call him
away. But the tiny hand rested with the pressure of contented affection on Maynard's arm, and the dark eyes met
his downward glance with timid answering love.

There was no train of bridesmaids; only pretty Mrs.
Heron leaning on the arm of a dark-haired young man
hitherto unknown in Foxholm, and holding by the other
hand little Ozzy, who exulted less in his new velvet cap
and tunic than in the notion that he was bridesman to
Tin-Tin.

Last of all came a couple whom the villagers eyed yet
more eagerly than the bride and bridegroom : a fine old
gentleman, who looked round with keen glances that
cowed the conscious scapegraces among them, and a stately
lady in blue-and-white silk robes, who must surely be like
Queen Charlotte.

"Well, that theer's whut I call a pictur," said old
"Mester" Ford, a true Staffordshire patriarch, who leaned
on a stick and held his head very much on one side, with
the air of a man who had little hope of the present genera-

PLANNING THE WEDDING TOUR.

Kiesel.

tion, but would at all events give it the benefit of his criticism. "Th' yoong men noo-a-deys, the' 're poor squashy things — the' looke well but the' woon't wear, the' woon't wear. The' 're 's ne'er un 'll carry his 'ears like that Sir Cris'fer Chuvrell."

. . . .

At the church gate Mr. Bates was standing in a new suit, ready to speak words of good omen as the bride and bridegroom approached. He had come all the way from Cheverel Manor on purpose to see Miss Tina happy once more, and would have been in a state of unmixed joy but for the inferiority of the wedding nosegays to what he could have furnished from the garden at the Manor.

"God A'mighty bless ye both, an' send ye long laife an' happiness," were the good gardener's rather tremulous words.

"Thank you, Uncle Bates; always remember Tina," said the sweet low voice.

Wedding Day in Literature and Art

From "MR. BARNES OF NEW YORK"[1]

By ARCHIBALD CLAVERING GUNTER

THE sun is well up in the heavens when next morning Miss Anstruther, after an exquisite little yawn or two, finds she has been awakened by Marina's kisses.

"Bride's kisses!" she murmurs, and then ejaculates, "Ah! How perfect! How divine!"

For Marina is already in her bridal costume and looks a picture of blushing joy. Save the myrtle flowers that shade her heaving breast, everything about her dress is white, but Corsican; the graceful *mandile* ornamenting her dark hair, and the *faldetta* draping her beautiful figure.

"Quick! Enid!" cries the bride. "No more sleep to-day! Rosita will put your native costume upon you and make you a Corsican like me. Hurry! my bridesmaid, if you love me. I go now to receive Danella; during the ceremony he acts as my father." And she runs excitedly to the portico.

A few minutes after Rosita comes to Marina, laughs and says, "The English young lady wishes to see you."

She darts to her, and finding Enid not yet dressed, asks, "What's the matter?"

"Matter!" cried the English girl; "despair's the matter! I've used twenty hairpins and look at my *mandile*."

"Of course. No one but a native can arrange that," laughs Marina; she seizes Enid, and her dexterous hands soon put the finishing touches to that young lady's toilet. "Now!" she cries, leading her to a mirror, "behold a Corsican!"

"Oh!—ah!" says Enid. "I wonder if my dressmaker did n't think it was for a fancy ball — it 's — it 's so awfully short."

" Not at all," answers Marina — " no shorter than mine — and in it you are a fairy."

" Y-e-s, it is becoming," murmurs Enid, taking a meditative blushing glance at herself. " To tell you the truth, it 's wonderfully fetching ; when you 're in Corsica, do as the Corsicans do. — All the same, I feel as if I were a ballet girl."

" Then come to breakfast or the ballet will begin without you," laughs Marina, carrying Enid off, who thinks to herself how Burton would admire her in the dress, and makes up her mind it would be just the costume for an English fancy ball.

Half an hour afterwards, Enid runs into Marina's room crying, " Here 's Fra Diavolo himself ! " and drags her to the portico ; where they see the count just riding up, dressed in full Corsican costume, an eagle's feather in his hat. He is followed by several young native gentlemen in the gala dress of the island. They are introduced to Enid ; and one, a dark-eyed, strong-limbed young man, who is to make the address to the bride, places his bright eyes upon Miss Anstruther with an apparent wish to take the place of the absent Barnes.

But he has little time for this, as very shortly after their arrival a great shouting is heard; and a band of goat-herds from the count's estates on the Monte Rotondo, clad in skins and armed with double-barrel guns, come up the avenue, followed by half the peasants of the village of Bocognano, to escort the bride to the house of her husband. For the count, in order that the ceremony may be conducted in true Corsican form, has placed his mansion for the day in possession of the bridegroom.

A couple of Corsican horses, with bridles and saddles gaily decked with myrtle and ribbons, are led out for the young ladies to ride.

But before the bride is permitted to depart from her home, every one gathers about her to hear the farewell address that, according to ancient custom, the young cavalier who acts as bridesman makes Marina upon her leaving her native *commune*.

.   .   .   .

After a little the count distributes among the villagers gifts of money as a souvenir for the *commune*, and whispering to Marina, "Anstruther will be impatient for you," places the bride in her saddle; the same office being done for Enid by young Signor Bernardo, who struts proudly about, feeling that he has distinguished himself. . . .

The wedding procession is soon formed in ancient Corsican style; a spinning-wheel made gay with flowers and ribbons, the emblem of a fruitful marriage, being borne before the bride; and with great firing of guns from the men, and throwing of rice, flowers, fruits, and wheaten spears from the women, they go off on the dusty road, along the little village street, under a great arch of evergreens, brightened with flowers and festooned with gaudy ribbons. And so with mandolins thumbing at their head they finally come up the avenue of olive-trees that brings them to the count's great house on the hillside, where a number of country magnates are gathered with the bridegroom, awaiting the coming of the bride.

Unmindful of local etiquette, which in this island sentences the bridegroom to be bashful, Anstruther, the moment he sees Marina, springs down the steps and seizing her in his arms kisses her before the concourse and calls her his wife so tenderly, that the girl forgets everything in her happiness at the thought that now they need part no more.

Then he stands by her side, his simple English naval uniform in marked contrast to the picturesque native costumes about him, every now and then saying a merry word to Enid or Marina as the usual speeches are made; the count demanding, in their quaint ancient way, of the bridesman : If he and his companions are the accepted escort of the gentle lady that they bring with them to his house.

Signor Bernardo, answering for himself and his follow-ing, declares that they are friends of the beautiful Marina, and have escorted her from affection to present her as the flower of Bocognano to a noble English gentleman as his spouse; and that they are all good and true men, and no enemies, as they fire their guns with no bullets in them.

The count being finally persuaded that they are not bandits, invites Bernardo and his companions to the wedding festivities; and after this the whole concourse go to the little stone chapel in the hamlet, where Marina Paoli becomes the wife of Edwin Anstruther, promising to love him and do him honour, after the ritual of the Holy Roman Church.

. . . .

And, this being over, and the various legal documents being signed both by priest and notary, the crowd goes back again with more firing of guns, and music, and shouting, to the count's great house, where the banquet is spread for all comers; and that being finished, with much drinking of wine, and speeches of congratulation and joyous laughter, the ball begins, at which the youths and maidens perform the *tarantella*, *marsiliana*, and other national dances, to the music of the *mandoline* and *citera*.

Then, just after the evening has grown dark, the guests with many little peculiar Corsican customs wish the bridal couple good luck and happy union, and depart along the hill-paths and through the olive and chestnut woods to their homes, as the fires of good omen are lighted on the summits of the neighbouring mountains.

Looking at this, Miss Anstruther says to her brother, "To-day has been to me like a Roman carnival."

"Theatrical, was n't it!" replies Edwin. "But I've got her — she is mine — and that's enough for my earthly happiness;" and he gives a very proud and very fond glance at Marina, who, at a little distance from him, on the great portico that fronts the house, is holding consultation with Danella. "However, since you like romantic effects, Enid, we'll have all the yokels at Beechwood dressed up as American cowboys and backwoodsmen to follow Mr. Barnes and you to church next month, in dear old Hampshire; and may you be as happy and fortunate as I."

"Fancy Diggs the sexton's astonishment at cowboys coming up the aisle," laughs Miss Anstruther. "Your idea is worthy of consideration."

A Daughter of Heth

From "A DAUGHTER OF HETH"

By WILLIAM BLACK

AND so it was that on a fresh June morning, when the earth lay warm and silent in the bright sunshine, and the far sea was blue and clear as the heart of a sapphire, Coquette arrayed herself in white garments. There was a great stir about the manse that morning, and the boys were dressed in their Sunday clothes. Flowers were all about the place; and many innocent little surprises in the way of decoration had been planned by the Whaup himself. The manse looked quite bright, indeed; and Leezibeth had assumed an unwonted importance.

Coquette's bridesmaids were the Misses Menzies, and the Doctor was there too, and Lady Drum and Sir Peter. According to the custom of the country, the marriage was to take place in the house; and when they had assembled in the largest room, the bride walked slowly in, followed by the bridesmaids.

In a church, amid a crowd of spectators, there would have been a murmur of wonder and admiration over the strange loveliness of the small and delicately modelled woman, whose jet-black tresses and dark and wistful eyes seemed all the darker by reason of the snowy whiteness of her dress and the paleness of the yellow blossoms and pearls that shone in the splendid luxuriance of her hair. But her friends there almost forgot how lovely she was in regarding the expression of her face — so immovably calm it was and sad. Lady Drum's heart was touched with a sudden fear. This was not the look of a bride; but the look of a woman — strangely young to have such an expression — who seemed to have abandoned all hope in this world. She was not anxious or perturbed or pale through any special excitement or emotion; she stood throughout the long and tedious service as though she were unconscious of what was happening around her, and, when it was over, she received the congratulations of her friends as though she had awakened out of a dream.

The Whaup, too, noticed this look; but he had seen much of it lately, and was only rendered the more anxious to take her away and lighten her spirits by change of scene. And now he saw himself able to do that, he was full of confidence. There was no misgiving in his look. As he stood there, taller by a head than his father, with his light brown hair thrown carelessly back from a face bright with health and the tanning of the sun, it was apparent that the atmosphere of the great city had not had much effect upon the lithe and stalwart and vigorous frame. And his voice was as gentle as that of a woman when he went forward, for the first time after the ceremony, and said to Coquette, —

"You are not tired with standing so long, Coquette ?"

She started slightly. Then — perhaps noticing that the eyes of her bridesmaids were upon her, and recollecting that she ought to wear a more cheerful expression — she smiled faintly, and said : "You must not call me by that foolish name any more. It is part of the old time when we were girl and boy together."

"But I shall never find any name for you that I shall like better," said he.

About an hour thereafter all preparations had been made for their departure; and the carriage was waiting outside. There was a great shaking of hands and kissing and leave-taking; and then, last of all, the Minister stood by the door of the carriage as Coquette came out.

"Good-bye, my dear daughter," he said, placing his hand on her head; "may He that watched over Jacob, and followed him in all his wanderings with blessings, watch over you and bless you at all times and places ! "

Coquette's lips began to tremble. She had maintained her composure to the last; but now, as she kissed her uncle, she could not say farewell in words; and when at length she was driven away, she covered her face with her hands and burst into tears.

From " MITO YASHIKI : A TALE OF OLD JAPAN "[1]

By ARTHUR COLLINS MACLAY, A.M., LL.B.

KONISHI complained of a headache and remained at home. The day was very warm. So he placed a mat upon the grass beneath one of the magnificent cryptomeria that so deeply shaded the terrace, and lay there meditatively smoking his pipe and gazing down through the trees on the blue waves beneath. Finally, he appeared to have been smitten with a brilliant idea, for he eagerly called to the abbot, who was lounging on the veranda, to come out and keep him company. That jovial gentleman was always ready to converse with his intelligent guest, and at once hastened to spread his mat also beneath the shade-trees. After having exhausted quite a number of topics of conversation, Konishi suddenly turned to his companion and said in a grave voice, —

" I have something of great importance to communicate to you. It is a matter wherein I shall need your friendly assistance. Can I rely on having it ? "

" Surely, surely ! " replied the abbot, somewhat taken aback. " I very willingly place my humble services at your disposal. Whether I can aid you much or not remains to be seen."

" Be quite easy on that point," replied Konishi, " for I have carefully considered the point and feel that your services will be of the utmost benefit to me."

" What will be the nature of the services ? " languidly inquired the abbot, after a pause which he had improved by taking several brisk whisks from his pipe.

[1] *By permission of G. P. Putnam's Sons, from " Mito Yashiki " by A. C. Maclay.*

THE MARRIAGE BUREAU.

Daelen.

" I wish you to act as a go-between to negotiate a marriage for me," replied Konishi, with charming bluntness and a mischievous smile.

The startled priest looked incredulous at this announcement. He, a priest sworn to celibacy, negotiate a marriage contract! Shades of Kobu-Daishi! What could this mean? Was protracted loneliness making the young man crazy? Konishi laughed at his friend's confusion and then tapped him on the shoulder and exclaimed: " Don't be frightened, austere and holy priest, for I shall not ask you to speak to the lady herself. Her father is living, therefore your communications will be addressed to him. This will remove all awkwardness from the situation. . . . I have long loved the daughter of Mr. Nakashima, and do now desire to make her my wife and carry her back to Mito. Now will you kindly favour me by interviewing the old gentleman and obtaining his consent to the match? I imagine the young lady will not be shocked by the proposal, for she has manifested increasing kindness towards myself during many weeks past, so that I am inclined to think that she and I are in the same predicament and that we both need go-betweens. What say you ? "

" I will arrange matters this very afternoon," was the hearty response.

.   .   .   .

The appointed day came around and the feast was spread in the reception room. It did great credit to the ingenuity of the cook. The limited nature of the market rendered it impossible to have over a dozen courses, but the *sake* was most excellent, and the good-fellowship unbounded. None were present save the members of the family and the abbot. It may seem incredible, yet the presence of strangers was hardly noticed by the monks. In those days it was a common thing for fugitives escaping from the vengeance of political adversaries to fly to the monasteries for protection. So that when our party of fugitives had settled themselves in the house of the abbot, the only comment provoked by this event was that they were merely political refugees. That explained everything to the satisfaction of everybody, and no further questions were asked and no acquaintanceship was sought. Consequently our friends were as much strangers as on the day of their arrival. The feast progressed, nevertheless, with great *éclat*. The bride and groom drank from the same cup and duly were declared man and wife amid the usual banterings. Late in the afternoon the entertainment came to an end.

Then the happy couple prepared to depart. The *kago* was ready at the gate, and the boat was ready on the shore. After a season of protracted farewells the ladies finally surrendered the bride to her husband to be carried off. The children were greatly grieved at her departure, for she had indeed made herself one of them, with her sprightly ways and joyous temperament. After she had been tenderly packed in her *kago* the gentlemen escorted her down to the shore. The road was exceedingly steep and rugged. It wound down through most magnificent scenery. Although the distance traversed was not over twenty miles, yet it was late in the evening before they reached the deep inlet where the boat had been moored. It was a bright moonlight night, however, so they were enabled to embark without difficulty. The scullers then made for the open sea, where the sails were quickly spread, and the wings of the southwest monsoon bore them rapidly up the coast towards the bridegroom's home.

The Beads of Tasmer

From "THE BEADS OF TASMER" [1]

By AMELIA E. BARR

IT was in the early days of autumn that Donald brought home his bride, — those golden September days when the air is fine and subtle, and the amber rays shine through the shimmering branches. The castle garden was full of the splendid glories of dahlias and hollyhocks, of the scents of sweet-brier and southernwood, and of all kinds of nameless perfumes, — emanations of the earth, of the trunks of trees, of the ripened fruit, of the turning foliage. Old ocean laughed with incalculable dimples. The birds were singing their latest songs in the woods. From the church-tower in the village the bells sent forth a grave, sweet harmony, dilating in the air, wandering up to the castle-turrets and far out to sea. As the morning advanced, a soft yellow light fell like a glorious veil over earth and ocean, making the mountains more like clouds at sunsetting than real things.

There had been in Edinburgh a solemnly quiet, religious ceremony, in which Minister Balfour himself joined the hands of his daughter and Sir Donald Torquil. Only Sara and Maclane and a few of Roberta's kindred had been present. A very blissful service it had been, and Donald and Roberta, for themselves, could have desired no nobler, no more blessed sacrament of their love than that touching service in the manse parlour.

But others had to be taken into consideration, and it was necessary for the Torquil to take his bride also by the ancient faith, in which his fathers had lived and died; and so, by its blessing, make Roberta indeed mistress of Tasmer. In a little gray church where the old religion had built itself

[1] By permission of Robert Bonner's Sons, from " The Beads of Tasmer," by Amelia E. Barr.

a shrine, even in the city of John Knox, Father Contach was waiting for them. With infinite love and solemnity he joined their hands in the irrevocable tie of the Church. And thus they went forth to their new life, with its obligations bound to them by holy prayers, and its delights sanctified by holy blessings.

It had been resolved to hold the bride-feast in Tasmer, and to call all the clan and all the neighbours together for this festival. Sara and Maclane took charge of the preparations for this home-coming, and Nature crowned them with the gift of a few days of heavenly beauty. Early on the morning of the happy day, the rising mist revealed the Minch covered with boats, all making for Torquil pier. They were filled with men in their Sabbath clothing, and with women in white caps, and lasses snooded with ribbons. For every man, woman, and child of the Torquil blood, and all the Torquils who had intermarried with the Mac-Farlanes or the Mackenzies, were coming to Sir Donald Torquil's bridal feast.

They filled the cottages to overflowing, and found amusement enough in the fact of their rare meeting and in watching the constant arrival of the gentry in trig yachts or in fine carriages. At ten in the morning the bells rang out, and Father Contach was seen in the street of the village, talking to a Torquil from Cairndow or Bundalloch, or listening to a tale of joy or sorrow from some girl whom he had, perhaps, christened, confirmed, and married.

When the full glory of the noontide was over sea and land, Donald's carriage was seen at the top of the hill, a mile away. Then old Hector, leaning on the arm of Father Contach, went and stood at the entrance of the village to bless and welcome *the Torquil* and his bride. The people, with that mannerly behaviour which belonged to their temperament and education, ranged themselves along the roadside with smiling faces, casting handfuls of heather or ripe wheat or sweet-smelling broom in the path of the bride's carriage. Their gentle blessing lingered in the still, golden atmosphere, and came to Roberta and

MARITAL BLISS.
Volkhart.

Donald with the perfume of the flowers and the heavenly echoes of the church-bells.

When they reached the fir-wood, all sounds became a softened, tremulous murmur of gladness. Hector was in a carriage with Father Contach, but the people spread themselves before and behind and on each side in the green shades — the fishers, feeling as if they were in a new world, solemnised by the tender, mystical light, and gravely curious about the birds and insects, of which the sea had taught them nothing.

Long tables had been laid for them in the big granaries, and there already Malcolm Roy's magic violin was heard calling them together in those plaintive or delirious strains which not a heart among them could resist. As the day passed on, the sense of festival grew stronger. The courts were full of carriages and servants. Men known through all the country-side, and richly garmented women, strolled among the late flowers, or sauntered in the newly adorned rooms of the castle. The tones of music, of low laughter, of rippling conversation, and the *froufrou* of silken robes, intoxicated the spirits like wine. And Sara was everywhere present, full of joy and welcome, to both peers and peasants : her dress of blue velvet, her shimmering pearl necklace, her coronal of bright hair, her charming manners, making her a conspicuous and delightful hostess.

At length the magnificent dining-hall was thrown open, and all its splendid space was thronged with guests of honour or renown. Then Donald led in the lovely woman whom he had made Lady of Torquil. A murmur, indescribable and irrepressible, ran through the pleased assemblage. Had such a pearl, indeed, come out of the fishing village of Ellerloch? For Roberta's girlish beauty had merely indexed the superb loveliness of her maturity. Within the past year she had improved marvellously ; for, in love and hope and joyful confidence, beauty grows to its perfection.

She was tall enough to be mate for Donald's lofty stature; and her fine countenance, with its wide, white brow and shining eyes and glorious colouring, reflected a soul full of tenderness, intellect, and generosity. A robe of rich white satin clothed her. It had borders of silver-work, and the sapphires of Tasmer gleamed on her white throat and wrists, and clasped the supple silver zone which marked her waist. Orange-blossoms crowned her dark hair and lay among the laces at her bosom. Every heart bowed down to her — every tongue praised her.

When the wedding toast was drunk, the whole people came in. They stood around the hall in rows four deep, and when Father Contach blessed the bride-cup and lifted it toward heaven, five hundred cups were lifted with it, and the murmur of the "*Amen*" was a music that smote each heart beyond the power of speech, beyond all human interpretation, but such as eyes shining through tears may give.

From "OUT OF TOWN"[1]

By ROSINA EMMET SHERWOOD

THE preparations for Mary's wedding naturally raised a tremendous stir in the Miller household, and the young couple soon found that they were to have no voice in the final arrangements. Mr. Miller, after consulting with every ticket agent, conductor, and brakeman on the railroad, made out a dozen different schedules for trains for the transportation of the guests, and then found that his wife had settled the matter two weeks before, and was having the invitations engraved, with cards giving full directions about trains, hours, and so forth. Uncle Chad bustled about giving suggestions, which Mrs. Miller passed by unheeded. She was calmly sure of her own superior knowledge about wedding celebrations, and felt strong to grapple with the subject unaided by the men of the family.

The day before the wedding Uncle Chad took Mary aside and handed her a large blue envelope which contained a deed of the land for her new home and a number of securities. He was sorry, he said, that his present was not more showy, but explained apologetically that it was not a bad thing for young people to start in life backed up by "the elegant simplicity of the three-per-cents."

They had a fine day for the wedding. Uncle Chad, De Vinney, and Little Marian wept steadily through the ceremony in the church, but made up for it afterwards by noisy demonstrations of joy at the reception. Dick Parker, Harford's friend from Wyoming, a retiring bronzed young man of stalwart frame, acted as best man, and was much disconcerted by Miss Lavinia Miller's attentions. She followed him about with a cold and critical eye, and, with her head on one side, walked round him and studied him from

1 From "*Out of Town,*" *published by Harper & Brothers.*

various points, with a view to using his type for some of her illustrations.

Mr. Johnstone Leigh, faultlessly attired, leaned gloomily against one of the piazza posts, occasionally bowing ceremoniously to the passers-by, while Mr. Billy Merriam circulated about among the guests, explaining to each one of his friends that this was one of the slickest picnics he ever was to.

De Vinney presented to the bride a photographic group of the hook-and-ladder company, framed in black walnut with gilt scrolls, and told her that he had arranged for the Starling Bicycle Brigade to escort the bride and groom to the station, the wheels to be decorated with white wedding-favours. This ceremony was with difficulty averted at the last moment. Tommy Mason, surrounded by the young cousins, sang all the latest music-hall songs; and Uncle Chad, who had had several glasses of some fine Hector Madeira which he had reserved for Mary's wedding, trolled out in his deepest bass " In Good Old Colony Days," and, to the great delight of the children, wound up by leading the Virginia Reel on the lawn, and then dancing the Sailor's Hornpipe in great shape.

Miller scurried about among the carriages, gave directions to the waiters, looked at his watch a great many times, and, aided by Miss Lavinia and Professor Judd, took various photographic views of the bridal party. Finally, amid loud cheers and the usual rice and slippers, Harford and his bride drove away, with little Jack seated in triumph on the box by the coachman, holding the whip, and Henry Marsh hanging on behind, followed at a distance by his shrieking mother.